*Animal Migration*

A SUN BOOK

# Animal Migration

RENÉ THÉVENIN

Translated from the French by Noel Kenton

A SUN BOOK

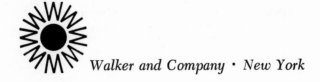

Walker and Company · New York

# Preface

A *migration,* if we use this word in its narrowest etymological sense, means, strictly speaking, a change of residence.

However, the term's exact meaning depends, to some extent, on whether it is applied to human displacements, or to those of animals. As regards the first, it usually implies a large-scale movement of a people who take themselves to a new country with a view to a prolonged or permanent stay. But in the case of animals, with which we are solely concerned, it means rather a periodic journey and a more or less regular return. In fact, this is the most general rule; but as we shall see, it admits of quite a number of exceptions.

In principle, the migratory animals form the majority, and setting aside those that do not have individual locomotion, only a small number are truly sedentary.

For a long time, however, the opposition opinion was generally held, because the displacements are often effected only at a slow rate, with no one keeping track of them and staking out the stages with the necessary perseverance.

In contrast, some arrivals and departures are so obvious, so punctual and accompanied by circumstances so remarkable that they cannot escape the most casual attention; and commonly only the animals involved in them are thought of as migratory.

Above all, this is true of the swallow. Apart from its traditional reputation, some observant spirits have given it a monopoly of the characteristic, by refusing to allow it to some related species, which, however, have it in the same degree, or nearly so. And indeed La Fontaine contrasted this nomad—consenting, it is true, to couple it with "the duck, the crane and the woodcock"—to the little birds by making it undertake journeys upon which it "learned a great deal," while the others, presumably, knew nothing, since they never left home.

What is more, this was the view of a man who delighted in studying nature. And if the example he chose seemed to him so striking and evident, what can be said of some of the astonishing explanations that have been given for the swallows' disappearance and reappearance, some of which are still current today?

We will have more to say on this matter when we come to examine the causes that provoke migratory movements in the different animal species. But for the present, the simple fact that divergencies of opinion exist in a case so directly verifiable will indicate that agreement is still further away when we attempt to interpret, as a whole, the determining causes of the phenomena we intend to examine here. Why animals migrate is a question that immediately raises a whole host of answers; and that they should be so numer-

ous certainly seems to suggest that none of them is absolutely satisfactory. Or, if we prefer to put the same thing
in less misleading terms, each answer contains a part of the
truth, but only a part.

It might seem logical to review these different hypotheses before describing the types and habits of the animals
that give rise to them. But instead we shall follow the opposite course, because by watching the greater part of these
creatures in action, and by studying their behavior, we shall
often have the impression of discovering for ourselves the
motives that control them, so obvious and indisputable do
certain of these seem. Otherwise it might be said, Why
bring up all these theories, which conflict and oppose one
another, when, merely by examining the facts, the evidence
leaps to the eye? We shall several times have cause to ask
ourselves questions of this sort, and at first glance we shall
have seen all we need to see to solve the problem, without
having to complicate its unnecessarily. However, if we press
our inquiry a little further, we shall discover quickly enough
that we do not always have a reason for being so sure, that
things are not always as straightforward as they seem, and
that our explanations do not always dispel the obscurity of
enigmas.

And naturally it is the mystery of those shadowed areas
that most excites our curiosity!

We have said that the majority of animals are migrants.
Then why not choose one of them as an example for
all?

For a start, we must distinguish between the great

travelers—such as our classic example, the swallow—and the erratics, those that move by no well-defined stages, sometimes roaming, sometimes loitering in places where they find nourishment and security, delaying to graze or sleep, only resuming their journey when food grows scarce or when disturbed by a suspected danger, and then never going very far before again coming to a standstill.

This is true of many mammals, although not all.

Taken as a whole, mammals always appear to inhabit the same country and the same district; this is often true of the most important of them as well as the most insignificant. A tiger, for instance, has his recognized territory, in which he stays, and in which, as a matter of principle, he never suffers the intrusion of a rival. As long as nothing disturbs him, we can be sure of finding him there again either a year or many years later.

Nevertheless, and quite apart from being a rare enough exception, even this sedentary will more than once be obliged to move on, against his will, because his prey moves on and he must follow it or die of hunger.

A superficial observation might suggest that this prey, in turn—antelope or deer, if we like—is no traveler either, and that he will always live in the district where he was born, as if enclosed there. But this is not so at all, and we know that one of the chief difficulties of keeping a given species in a zoological reserve arises precisely from this need to wander, this need for a change of air that affects even those animals that look the most firmly fixed. No doubt, after making a more or less extensive circuit, they always end up by returning to the place where they were first observed;

but this does not detract from the need to accomplish this circuit, and it is a *migration*, pure and simple. Nor does it matter much whether the movement is fast or slow, regular or random, distant or local. The need exists, and, we repeat, the majority of animals are subject to its law.

However, more often than not, this law is observed within the limits we have just defined, and to indicate the conditions applying to one species suffices to show that they are applicable in the same ways to many others. This will recur whenever a species is studied: what applies to it will also apply to others in their turn.

On the other hand, in certain zoological groups some genera and families are obviously much more infected than their neighbors with this nomadism that urges them on irresistibly, or according to a kind of inevitable rhythm, toward other climates. And we know that much the same urges are evinced in man himself.

The field has been surveyed, and now we propose to examine some individual cases.

RENÉ THÉVENIN

# Contents

*Animal Migration*

**A SUN BOOK**

# 1 / Migratory Movements
## In Some Invertebrates

### The Eighth Plague

Just as we have taken the swallow to be the most popular
example of the migrant bird, so can we find its equivalent
in the insect world, provisionally claiming this distinction
for the locust, to start with a creature known to everyone.

Its fame is not new. A chapter of the Bible is devoted
to it, and it is described with a scientific precision rarely
found in the Scriptures, as far as species of animals are
concerned.

> . . . and the Lord brought an east wind upon the land
> all that day, and all that night; and when it was morning,
> the east wind brought the locusts. And the locusts went up
> over all the land of Egypt, and rested in all the coasts of
> Egypt: very grievous were they; before them there were
> no such locusts as they, neither after them shall be such.
> For they covered the face of the whole earth, so that the
> land was darkened; and they did eat every herb of the

land, and all the fruit of the trees which the hail had left: and there remained not any green thing in the trees, or in the herbs of the field, through all the land of Egypt.

Exodus 10: 13–15

For once, in these lines, the sacred book does not allow itself to be overpowered by poetic emphasis, and the terms it uses to describe the effects of the eighth plague inflicted by Moses on Pharaoh's kingdom are hardly exaggerated. At their worst, they spread the scourge over the whole of Egypt, and this darkness that covered the land, these fruits of which not one was left on the trees, and this grass that vanished from the fields, are no more than firm facts, which since then have been repeated some thousands of times.

Locusts are certainly the cause of this. Or, to be more exact, the culprits are various species of Orthoptera belonging to the Acridiidae. For simplicity's sake we will treat them as a group under the name commonly used in everyday speech: "migratory crickets."

These species are quite numerous, and they vary according to the countries in which they are encountered. If those of Europe, Asia and North Africa differ little from each other, other types are found in equatorial Africa and South Africa, while Madagascar, the Philippines, North and South America, and Australia—since this formidable insect has spread over the entire globe—have their particular indigenous types.

The fact that the same species can present an appearance and characteristics very different in the various phases of its development complicates the problem, since sometimes the identical insect is classified under several different names. Moreover, the opposite occurs, and with more obvious inconvenience, for each species has its own particular habits and conditions of life, and as we shall see, these must be thoroughly understood if we are effectively to combat the scourge.

Crickets are distinguished from the hunting Orthoptera by their long hind legs, formed for jumping, and from grasshoppers, which share the same characteristic, by their thick short antennae, and by the absence in the females of the projecting ovipositor, which prolongs the abdomen and serves, during egg-laying, to convey the cluster of eggs into the soil. Several species are common in France, and everyone, perhaps without knowing their names, has seen, in wild country or among the sand dunes of the seashore, the pretty Oedipodae, such as *Oedipoda coerulescens,* with its turquoise wings, or the bright-pink *Oedipoda miniatra,* bounding from underfoot and covering several yards in a single, quivering leap.

These insects, like all Orthoptera, do not undergo a complete metamorphosis—as, for example, do butterflies and flies—but pass by easy stages and through several molts from the larval form to the adult form, without stopping at the nymphal stage. They have four wings, and the leathery front pair covers the other pair, which, when at rest, folds up like a fan. The males have a stridatory organ, and both sexes have on the first abdominal segment a membrane that is sensitive to sound, and that connects to the nervous system and a network of trachea. As to the means by which these organs hear, and above all, just what they hear, we so far have no notion.

In their most usual state crickets live in isolation, even when there are numbers of them in the same region, or rather, they live independently of one another; and in those conditions, what damage they can do passes unnoticed, because they keep up a steady average of depredation, and the over-all situation shows no change.

However, for reasons that long remained mysterious, and that are only now beginning to be understood, a moment comes when these solitary individuals come together and group themselves into masses whose numbers seem to defy human calculation, then, in unison, they take flight and make a perilous journey in a given direction, until at length they settle in an area of their choice, leaving the land over which they have passed totally bare.

Figures are often quoted in regard to these migrations, but like those dealing with outer space, they end by leaving little impression, so enormous are they.

Troops of locusts in serried ranks covering a plain of 230 square miles; clouds of locusts passing over without pause for several days; cohorts of locusts, whose effective strength, calculated from the weight of a sample of them, equals that of 50 billion men; ten times this figure for the locusts' egg-potential, calculated at a hundred eggs per egg-sac collected; loss to agriculture in the United States estimated at 250 million dollars in ten years—we can see that the biblical account does not exaggerate in the least, and that the nations periodically menaced by locusts could long ago have better defended themselves against them if only they had persevered in their efforts, and had employed some systematic method, without relaxing each time the danger passed.

It should be said, however, that up to the last few years, this defense has at least been spectacular, and strongly reinforced with warlike apparatus—poison gas and flame-throwers—but this was more to appease the immediate grievances of a disgruntled electorate than with the idea of striking at the root of the evil and extirpating it. In another way, the means used recall, by their vigor, those employed in past centuries, which, less costly, have for their excuse a touching ingenuousness:

"I take"—the good monk Alvarez, who in the sixteenth century tried out the method in Abyssinia, informs us—"I take a number of these locusts and I perform an exorcism upon them . . . exhorting, admonishing, and excommunicating them. Then I order them to depart hence within three hours by winging their way to the sea, or by taking the road to the country of the Moors and leaving Christian lands. If they refuse, I convoke all the birds of the sky, all the animals of the earth, and all the tempests of the air, and adjure them to devour, destroy and disperse the locusts."

On the whole, we would not insist here on these defense procedures if research had not produced the results mentioned above, which to some extent have lifted the veil that still hides the "mystery" of the migrant locusts from our eyes.

Associated with this work are the names of B. P. Uvarov, Zolotarevsky and P. Vayssière, as well as those of a host of field observers in several countries who, although still a long way from any conclusions, have at least shown us the paths that should be followed, and who, in a few years, have made more progress with the problem than had been made for centuries.

For a start, these scientists have established that all the migratory locusts appear under different forms following a continuous series from the time of the insects' solitary and sedentary life, to the time when they become gregarious and migratory, by passing without clearly evident demarcations through a succession of transitional forms.

Although each of these intermediary states—*transiens,* as they are called—is closely similar to that which immediately precedes it and that which follows it, there are some characteristics so specifically peculiar to the extreme phases that, until recently, they were attributed to different species, some of which were described as never being gregarious and migratory, while others were described as always being so. It was never realized that the question at issue concerned one and the same animal at different periods of its life.

A revision of the classification of the group resulted, but this was not the principal interest of the discovery.

Continuing the researches, it was established that the individual locusts studied at the time of the solitary phase were dispersed over immense stretches of territory—for instance, throughout the Old World, where this type lived permanently, and which constituted its *area of habitat.* On the other hand, at certain less extensive points of these same territories were to be found the *gregarigenic areas,* that is to say, not regions that invariably offer the locusts the necessary conditions for massing into migratory hosts, but areas containing even more restricted zones, which can, in certain circumstances, constitute *focal points*. These, on a given occasion, will provide all the elements indispensable for the formation of teeming swarms and for their next flight.

What are these circumstances? It goes without saying that when we know them all, the problem of locust migration will be nearly solved. This migration seems to depend on an optimum degree of temperature, prevailing in localities where grow no trees, no bushes, not even any scrub: that is, in deserts, or rather, on scattered plots of land in the middle of deserts growing the gramineous plants— xerophils—peculiar to dry terrain that nourish the locusts' larvae. A significant number of gregarigenic areas have been identified; for example, the zone lying between the Niger River's flood area and the Sahel region of Upper Senegal, and particularly, the southern Sahara's littoral regions, which are exposed to the winter rains.

Moreover, other factors may intervene, checking the desire to migrate, or awakening it. Thus, when the young larvae, which begin to manifest the social instinct very early, approach superabundance and are ready to take off, parasites and predators, equally innumerable, descend upon them, and soon make such inroads in their ranks that the locusts, decimated, are finally cured of the migratory fever (which only shows itself when there is enough density to insure effective strength). Then, as the destroyers' food supplies prove insufficient, they in turn disappear. The egg-laying of the adult locusts is renewed with greater activity, the larvae again become superabundant and, provided the other necessary conditions obtain, the gregarious instinct reappears.

To know all this is to know a great deal, but much remains to be learned. Why, and by what means, do the locusts react to these influences? What force is it—emanating on occasion from certain shrubs and sedges south of the 15th Parallel, given particular conditions of temperature, humidity and atmospheric pressure—what force is it that makes an animal thitherto of solitary habits suddenly acquire a gregarious nature and congregate with its fellows, which, like it, are all obedient to the same instinct at the same time, although preceding generations have never been subjected to it? At what moment does this assembly of independent individuals become a unanimous swarm, in which each seems no more than a single impassive cell in an immense body, carrying out all orders blindly, and reacting mechanically to a sort of invisible communal nervous system? Who gives the order to depart? Who decides what direction to follow? And who chooses the moment of landing? Or rather, what imperceptible physical or chemical occurrence instigates all these actions? Surely it is imprudent, and certainly misleading, to try to interpret the activities of these insects by comparing them with those of man, or as regards crickets, to think in terms of that "collective soul" displayed by human masses on certain occasions, when all individual will disappears, effacing individual personality. In any case, what do we really know about this collective soul? Very little, and if we cannot even define the motives of our own behavior, how can we hope to understand what activates beings who, as Professor Bouvier puts it, "never differ from us so much as when they seem most to resemble us"?

Thus, as soon as we look into the question of migratory groups, we realize that the explanation that at once springs to mind may not be the whole story. These insects set out *en masse*, we imagine, urged by hunger, when they find themselves too numerous for a particular area. But, if this is one of the determining causes—and is it yet certain that it is?—it is far from being the only one, and still further from being the essential one. As soon as we attempt to venture into these unexplored realms, we come upon fresh trails, which only make us lose our way.

Let us take one example out of many. In trying to understand our locust's behavior under the sway of its gregarious instincts, it seems we must not compare it with social insects—such as bees and ants—because they live as groups throughout their entire life span; on the other hand, in the neighboring world of spiders, certain specimens, such as the lycosae, stay closely united, appearing quite unable to separate during the first weeks of life, then suddenly, after molting, part company and disperse forever. And, indeed, it is after a quite insignificant process of molting that the crickets, from being individualists, become communists, forming an indivisible social bloc, and no longer maintaining their previous unparalleled type of existence. What takes place? What connection can there be between an insignificant change of skin and such a total transformation of instincts and habits?

It is an enigma among many, all just as disconcerting, and we are only beginning to understand them!

The locusts provide us with the outlines of problems that will recur as regards other migratory insects, and we will content ourselves by enumerating the chief examples of these without dwelling overly long on each. We still have plenty of other animal species to examine!

### Nomadic Butterflies

If the locust swarms have at all periods stirred man's imagination by the disproportion between their immensity and the insignificance of the individuals that constitute them, some journeys made by butterflies have also caused justified astonishment.

One species that has spread throughout the world, and is familiar to everyone, includes the Painted Lady (Linnaeus' *Pyrameis cardui*), which in our climate appears in June and again in the autumn, and is distinguished by its considerable size (5 to 6 cm), its tawny wings variegated by reddish-brown patches and black-and-white spots, and its caterpillars, found mainly on thistles, but also on artichokes, nettles, mallows and so on.

At very irregular periods—which can be separated by several years—these butterflies are seen traveling in large numbers, not in serried swarms like the locusts, but in small, connected groups, forming colonies several miles long, which comprise some millions, or tens of millions, of individuals.

In general, as far as Europe is concerned, these hosts appear to come from Africa, and consequently they cross the Mediterranean, where they can be met with in the open sea, flying more rapidly and, above all, in a more direct line, than one would expect of these insects, whose movements are normally so capricious and leisurely. Nor is the wind the cause of their speed, since they most often make these journeys against it.

The Painted Ladies are not the only Lepidoptera that have been observed in migrations of this kind. We could cite many others, among them the common cabbage white (*Pieris brassicae*), which can be seen in innumerable hordes crossing the Alps.

However, it is perhaps an American owlet-moth (*Alabama argillacea*), that ought to be considered the "star" in this category of migrants, as much for the number of participants as for the devastation caused. It has not been possible to determine just what influences induce these exoduses, but immense flights have been observed in Alabama, coming from the Gulf of Mexico, and then settling in the northwest regions of the United States, there creating havoc in orchards before, when the temperature drops, returning to the South—where the cotton crops harbor their caterpillars—and finally moving on down as far as Peru.

## Dragonflies and Some Others

It is doubtless less surprising to find the migratory instinct in dragonflies than in other insects, so perfectly adapted are they for flight, with their light, slender bodies and their powerful wings, whose structure offers such striking contrasts with those of the butterflies, contrasts not only anatomical but also physiological. Moreover, the group's larger species can be counted among the swiftest animals, not excluding birds.

Nevertheless, the dragonflies' speed potential does not seem to be exploited in the course of the journeys certain of them make, and an average speed of 7½ miles an hour has been estimated. Clearly, this is not much for a creature whose tremendous bursts of speed in its hunting activities many of us have admired.

On the other hand, the distances traveled appear to be considerable. Dragonfly migrations have been described leaving Asia Minor, or North Africa, and reaching England or Belgium; and such migrations have been encountered more than 300 miles from land.

In these circumstances the wind plays a part; but here again, as far as our latitudes are concerned, we most often observe the migrants taking off into the wind when it is from the west. They stay near the ground and travel in a number of flocks, which may extend for several miles. Normally, different species are observed mixed together in the swarm, and they may even be accompanied by flies and butterflies. The sea appears to influence these migrations, probably due to humidity—a favorable factor, since it is accompanied by some degree of warmth. Indeed, a drop in the temperature is enough to interrupt these migrations, or to stop them.

W. H. Hudson's graphic accounts of South America offer us some detailed observations of what he calls "dragonfly storms," which he witnessed in the pampas of Patagonia.*

These insects, Hudson says, only appear in advance of the *pampero,* the southwest wind that, violent, dry and cold, blows from the interior, swooping down suddenly and at any season of the year. The dragonflies, however, only appear in summer or autumn, and not with the wind, but ahead of it, flying at a speed of seventy to eighty miles an hour. Generally they precede the wind by about fifteen minutes, and the air—to a height of ten or twelve feet above the ground —all at once seems full of them. They rush past, with extraordinary speed, in a northeasterly direction.

As we mentioned in the case of the locusts, the question of food at once suggests itself as the chief cause of these migrations; and there is even a temptation to ascribe to the insects a sort of prescience, enabling them to escape a famine before it has even declared itself. However, by now we realize that we cannot be content with explanations of this sort.

Hudson in turn looked for an explanation, but, as he confesses, did not find one. The insects, he says, do not pass and repass between breeding and subsistence areas, but journey always in a southeasterly direction; and of the countless millions flying like thistledown before the *pampero,* not one solitary one ever returns.

The same author postulates that the flight has a dynamic cause, "affecting the insects with a sudden panic, and compelling them to rush away before the approaching

* The account of Hudson's findings that follows is paraphrased from his *The Naturalist in La Plata* (London: Dent, 1892).

tempest." However, it is quite probable that this again is a human interpretation, which need not detain us.

Among the most recent authors to tackle the problem, Grassé reports some interesting observations. He has noted that the migratory instinct develops at the moment when the pairs collect for breeding, and that the migrant groups are composed, in the main, of pairing insects. From this Grassé concludes that the stimulus of sexual maturity motivates the dragonflies, and that the direction of the migration is imposed on the entire group by that of the wind, that is, it is against it, in our climate. As for the mustering of the insects, it is provoked by mutual attraction, and also, perhaps, by imitation.

For the moment, let us merely note these hypotheses, since we shall have occasion to recall them when we come to the birds. Meanwhile, let us conclude by rapidly reviewing the insect world.

Together with these spectacular peregrinations, a number of other migrations must also be taken into account, since they involve displacements that, although much slower than those carried out by many species, are also much more important, when they involve the colonization of territories so far never occupied.

In the great majority of cases, man must be considered to have unleashed these expansionary movements, not only by involuntarily transporting the first invaders, but above all by offering them facilities for development that nature never provided.

"Humanity," says L. O. Howard, "has created conditions peculiarly favorable to certain kinds of insects, and they are multiplying as they never would have done had not man given them a chance." Then, apropos of this, Howard relates the story of the carrot rust fly:

> It seems that carrots in past years have never been a crop that counted for very much. In recent years, however, there has sprung up a great industry—the preparation of canned soups—and this has brought about a wide demand for carrots. As a result, these vegetables have been planted over large areas in central New York and elsewhere. One can guess what happened. A paradise for the carrot rust fly was created. A whole world of riotous living was opened before it. The destructive insect multiplied beyond measure. Dr. Glasgow expressed it in some such way as this: "Had the farmers been trying to raise rust flies instead of carrots, they could not, by the utmost ingenuity, have devised a better way."*

Some of the formidable invaders that have spread across the world would have stayed inoffensively in their original habitats if we had not induced them to leave. The Phylloxera and the Colorado beetle, to name only the most notorious, restricted their attentions respectively to wild vines and potatoes before they were attracted by the cultivated plants. Then they were transported with the plants to new lands, where they have multiplied on an extraordinary scale.

One example will suffice to give an idea of the rapidity of these encroachments. In 1866 the Phylloxera was noticed for the first time in France, on the stalks of some vines imported from America, in the village of Pujault (Gard), on

* L. O. Howard, *The Insect Menace* (New York: Appleton, 1931).

the right bank of the Rhone. Ten years later the insect had invaded the whole of the southeast, over an area forming a vast triangle with its base stretching from Béziers to Fréjus, and its apex reaching as far as Lyons!

With the San Jose scale, and some parasites of lesser importance, the Old World became the unwilling hosts to the New. But it was the Old World that started it, by conferring on the New the Hessian fly (*Mayetiola destructor*), the terrible gypsy moth (*Lymantria dispar*), the apple maggot (*Cydia pomonella*) and so on. One gift balances another, and all are products of civilization. In similar circumstances, concerning Honolulu, it has been said: "The mosquitoes and the missionaries arrived together."

These, however, are colonizers, rather than migrants, and we will not delay ourselves by discussing them, any more than we will say much about the termites or the ants, or even the bees, which no doubt also travel great distances, but do not belong to the category we propose to study here. However, before we leave the itinerant insects—and we shall even have to pass over some of these in silence— let us accord a final moment's attention to one of them, which offers a strange spectacle.

Imagine that we are in some forest of beeches or pines in Northern or Eastern Europe, and it is summer. Suddenly, as we happen to glance down, we see a strange creature gliding over the ground. At first glance we would say it was a sort of enormous flatworm, several meters long, eight to ten centimeters wide, and two to three millimeters thick, and as it advances it undulates with a slow and gentle movement.

If we look closer we see that we are not concerned with a single creature, but with a compact mass of "worms" of a sort, yellowish-white, and having a marked resemblance in color, shape and size to the gentles used by anglers for bait. These "worms" travel in such close-set order that, if a stick is used, a part of the mass can be lifted like the corner of a carpet, without its components at once separating.

Sometimes, however, an obstacle is too large not to divide this mass. But no time is lost in re-forming, and the delayed section redoubles its efforts in order to rejoin the procession's leaders. Sometimes the mass encounters a similar group, whereupon there is a moment of irresolution, and a little later the moving carpet is seen to have doubled its thickness, no longer forming a single mass.

In reality, these "military worms," "army worms," "snakeworms" and so on are the larvae of a dipteron of the Sciara genus (*Sciara militaris*), which migrates in this way when a particular set of circumstances, occurring but rarely, favors the breeding of great numbers and the consequent overcrowding of a given area.

## Aerodynamics in the Service of Migration

A few words must be said about some invertebrates other than insects whose journeys can be considered migrations.

Everyone is familiar with "gossamer"—those fine, silky threads that can be seen trembling in the air, keeping a more or less vertical position, and that in the spring and above all in the autumn, are sometimes extremely numerous.

No one any longer doubts that this gossamer is produced by spiders of various genera—Thomisidae, Augiopidae, Lycosidae and so on. But less is known of the various circumstances that stimulate and accompany its appearance.

Here again atmospheric conditions seem to play an important role in inducing the phenomenon, which is associated only with warm, cloudless days, and with that light mist which disperses before the gentlest breeze, and which assures the continuance of fine weather. Bucolic weather prophets take careful account of this gossamer, forecasting in rustic prognostications that tomorrow at least will be a day of sunshine.

If we continue with our study, we find that an infinite number of tiny spiders are hatched at the same moment, and are at once infected by great agitation. They scurry over the ground, and as soon as they come upon an object they can ascend—a bush or a clump of grass, a tree or a gatepost—they climb rapidly to the top of it, then become motionless. Now let us watch them closely.

Very soon we see them balancing on their front legs in order to raise the abdomen, which starts to spin its thread. This ascends vertically, thrust upward by the warm air rising from the ground. It goes higher, lengthening all the time, and when several yards have been spun, it starts to get caught up in horizontal air currents, which carry it with them.

This is the moment when the spider choose to let go, allowing itself to be carried away like a young girl in a romantic ballad. It is copied by millions of its sisters, who, as long as no hitch occurs that prematurely checks their flight, thus set out on a lengthy journey.

The principle is that of the free balloon. Some authors contend that the spider builds a tiny nacelle at the end of its thread, taking up the slack at will, at whatever moment it deems propitious for landing. Mac Cook, among others, vouches for the fact, and he is a shrewd and first-rate observer, "so much so that his statement cannot be rejected a priori, and we can only desire its confirmation."

L. Berland, from whom we borrowed the above detail and quotation, adds that the tiny female spiders, when they rise into the air, can reach a considerable altitude. "When flying I have encountered them at more than three thousand feet," he says, "and undoubtedly they can go much higher —it would not be surprising if they reached ten thousand feet, or even fifteen thousand. Meanwhile, the air currents carry them over more or less considerable distances, and even if we do not concede that they can land at will, the evening fall in temperature is sufficient to make them descend. At all events, they make their way, and this is their method of dispersing themselves. Which is the aim of this curious procedure. . . ."

Before leaving the world of the invertebrates, we should mention that there are still many examples to be found there—particularly among marine fauna—and pages could be written on the movements of the plankton, among others; or we could review the singular expansions of various crustaceans, such as the undesirable Chinese crab; or the periodic exoduses in countles masses of the cephalopods; or yet again, the strange nuptial dances of certain marine worms, coinciding so weirdly with the moon's phases.

Nevertheless a choice must be made. Other more familiar or more characteristic subjects await us. So now let's tackle them!

## 2 / The Migrations of Fish

Fish, since they are animals with an internal skeleton, a brain contained in an osseous cavity, and a vascular system of blood vessels conveying red blood, are related a little more closely to us than the creatures we have just studied.

Nevertheless the environment in which fish evolve is totally different from ours, and so, necessarily, are the reactions that environment induces; and the behavior of fish cannot possibly be explained if, for comparison, we take only our own actions and their determining motives.

In all ages, man, finding in the denizens of the ocean one of his most important food sources, has studied their habits closely, and from early on has drawn conclusions from his observations insofar as he understood them.

Frequently man has been deceived in his conclusions, and the wild hypotheses he has sometimes based upon them have by now all been abandoned. Nevertheless man has sometimes seen things correctly, and on the matter that now occupies us, he early realized that some kinds of fish live a settled existence, while others periodically come and go, and at the same time undergo profound changes of form and habit.

The salmon is certainly the most remarkable of these last, and it provides us with the best—indeed, the classic —example of a migratory fish.

## *The Salmon*

Let us say that we are not far distant from the source of a stream of clear running water, of such limpidity that we can see the sand and pebbles of its bed in spite of the glinting surface eddies. The water is cold, for winter is upon us, and now, in December, it is not impossible that tonight will bring a layer of ice to immobilize the stream's surface, while below the current will continue to run, preserving the minute and dormant lives entrusted to it.

Indeed, fish eggs, held among the pebbles, are everywhere, countless in this particular place, yet nearly invisible even if we can get right up to them, for they are transparent. They are quite large—the size of a pea in diameter—spherical, and heavy enough not to be swept away by the current, although they are not held by any filament or mucus.

These are the salmon's eggs.

But where are the females that laid them, the males that fertilized them? We explore the area in vain, and only with great difficulty do we at last come upon an adult of the species—sluggish, lusterless, weak, considerably emaciated, lacking half his scales, barely capable of reacting to his capture, failing which he would soon be a corpse, mauled by predatory animals. Is this the once brilliant, impetuous, powerful, splendid denizen of the river, the pride of the lower reaches? It is hard to think so!

Meanwhile the days go by, and presently the first breaths of early spring arrive to warm the eggs; and in them the latent life awakens. During the winter the embryos have developed, and now, as (in our climate) March approaches, the eggs hatch out and a tiny fish is released from each of the curved envelopes that have held it. Each fish, hardly formed, still transparent, immobile, keeps its stomach in contact with the ovular mass, which will continue to nourish it for some time, although the fish is quite free of it in all other respects.

By May the vesicle is exhausted, and the alevin starts to feed itself by mouth. It now measures a little over an inch, and gradually thickening, it becomes marbled with opaque spots. Progress continues briskly, and at the height of summer we can expect to find—save that its external appearance is altogether different from that of the adults—the lively fish we looked for in vain during the winter. That is to say, an agile and carnivorous little creature about two and two-fifths inches long, golden-brown, vanishing like an arrow if we make the slightest movement, reappearing just as fast as it leaps upstream in pursuit of its prey, and sharing this busy and dashing existence with its crowd of brothers, all identical.

The same fervor for living continues, and in the same places, until the third winter, when it abates slightly, and is accompanied by a slowing down of growth. Then, from the spring onward, the young salmon becomes vigorous again, and its activity reaches maximum when the fine weather comes, by which time it is about twenty months old. During the interval it has grown, and its appearance has changed a great deal, although it is still a long way from resembling its parents. Little by little its brown color has changed to a dark blue, while its belly has lightened to silver, and its sides have become marked by a line of blue spots on a rust-colored ground. The body is now six to seven inches long, and the fish is called a "smolt."

We have already pointed out that, as regards insects and spiders, the process of molting coincides with profound biological changes. Is this, then, a law? Are there certain chemical phenomena that condition these abstruse transformations? This is easy to believe, since we can see our smolts completely modifying their pattern of life, while as regards their habits, they become like different animals, so completely changed in behavior are they.

Nevertheless this law, if it is one, does not apply inevitably, for not all the young salmon hatched obey it at the same time. Several, although we do not know why, wait a further year, leading the same life as they have so far, without changing color again, and growing only slightly larger. These seem to be a minority.

We will concern ourselves only with the others. So far, each of them has been living close to his brothers, but this is due only to force of circumstances, and because there are a number of fish all in the same place. But there is nothing that can be called a social formation, a closely united group, such as we have seen among insects. At this point, however, such groupings start to form, growing stronger until they take on that characteristic demeanor of shoals of fish in which the movements are expressed in waves, as if the whole mass formed only a single body. And soon each school, leaving its native waters for the first time, and letting itself drift with the current, descends the stream until it gains the river and then the tideway, and so one day reaches the sea.

There the smolts pause for a while, as if wanting to get used to the new element that confronts them. They pause, letting themselves be swept seaward by the fresh water of the ebb tide, then once again ascend the estuary when the tide turns. Gradually, during the course of a week or two, they become acclimatized. Then suddenly, with a single accord, they make for the open sea.

As smolts they will never be seen again. Where do they go? What becomes of them? This is a problem still far from solved either by scientific research or by the experience of fishermen, and reasoned logic only begins to explain it. Clearly the fish make for deep water, plunging to depths that neither the trawl net nor the sounding line can easily reach; and when they return, they are, once more, completely transformed.

How do we know it is they that return? Because numbers of smolts caught in the estuaries have been marked, and then later, as salmon, have been caught again. A fish's age can be read by examining its scales (although it would take too long to explain the procedure here), and so the duration of its absence can be calculated. Findings of the following sort have been obtained:

A certain number of smolt that set out for the open sea in the spring return the following year from summer onward; now known as "grilse," they are completely transformed. The size of each fish has increased by five times, its weight by even more, and its appearance is totally different. Now a magnificent fish, twenty-four inches long and weighing about nine pounds, its back still retains its steel-blue color, but the spots that characterized the smolt are gone, and now the grilse's main coloring is silvery-pink. It is important to stress that these grilse of the first year are males, and that the bulk of the return, composed of both sexes, will not begin until the following spring or summer, and may even be delayed for two, three or four more years. Of course, these laggards will have grown considerably, and a distinction is made between the spring or summer salmon, weighing some thirteen pounds and measuring about 31.5 inches, and the big winter salmon, which return only between November and March, and can exceed a yard in length and thirty pounds in weight. Indeed, there have been reports of specimens weighing sixty pounds and more!

During the whole period of their absence the fish have devoted their efforts to feeding themselves, and as we can now see, they have been successful at it. Although we have no direct proof, their voracity during this period must be extraordinary, and its purpose is not solely that of growth and fattening, but above all—and we might say exclusively, since the increases in size and weight are only corollaries— of development and maturation of the genital organs.

In fact, whether female or male, the fish only return

in this way for purposes of reproduction, and the reserves of fat and energy they have accumulated in their bodies up to the time of spawning, have for their sole object the reinforcement of the sexual functions. Once the fish enters fresh water anew, it no longer feeds, but slowly ascends the river—taking a whole year for the journey if it is a winter salmon, several months if it is a summer one. Throughout this period it uses up its reserves by assigning their bounty to the benefit of its ovaries or its testes, at last reaching its destination swollen with eggs—thirty to forty thousand of them—or charged with milt, and having proportionately lost its weight of flesh, its firmness and its splendor.

This destination appears to be identical with the salmon's birthplace, that highest reach of a tiny tributary. The females rub their distended bellies against the pebbles of the spawning ground, at last expelling their eggs, and upon them the males shed their milt. Now they have played their part, and nothing remains for them but to waste away and vanish. The cycle starts again.

Most of these facts have been known for a long time, but as we begin to get familiar with them, queries spring up at every point concerning them. What is the reason for these immense journeys? How are they effected? Who assigns the young salmon to this deep-sea destination toward which they exert themselves, and this for the first time? What ineluctable force draws the adults back to the water of their birth? And so on, providing many interesting enigmas.

Before attempting these, let us examine other migratory

species. By means of comparisons and equivalents, perhaps we shall pick up a trace that will put us on the right trail.

## *Eels*

That is, unless it leads us entirely astray! Since, as regards the fish that we have now chosen to study—and that justifies our choice by reason of its habits, which are just as wayward as the salmon's—we find that the data are precisely reversed.

Whereas old-time observers early established the salmon's habits, the habits of the eel remained a mystery right up to the beginning of the present century, and the wildest hypotheses were proposed and persisted as explanations. To be fair, we must admit that the truth was difficult to discover.

The eels, once almost countless in the ponds and rivers, live in the same places for periods of years, in the upper reaches as well as in the estuaries (where they seem to be rather smaller, and have more pointed snouts). Then, one day, when they have reached a certain size, they disappear without giving us an inkling of what has become of them.

Soon, replacing them, others appear, all of them small. And this time we succeed in following their travels to some extent, from the moment when we see them appear on our coasts in their millions, forming innumerable clusters comparable to a sort of mobile vermicelli, each creature measuring some 2⅓ or 2¾ centimeters, weighing half a gram, transparent and having the diameter of a coarse thread. The fishermen of the estuaries collect these creatures by the basketful (without making any apparent impression on their numbers), and those not taken either settle in the river mouths or—and this applies to the greater part of them, known as "elvers"—make their way upstream, where they establish themselves, even colonizing ponds that they reach by crawling over the ground like snakes.

Certainly we can surmise that these elvers are tiny eels recently hatched. But from what eggs? From what hatcheries? Never, anywhere, have females containing eggs been met with, or males with milt; never, anywhere, have their spawning grounds been found. What are we to conjecture?

There is no lack of theories; there never is in such circumstances. It has been suggested that eels are viviparous, that they are formed in the intestines of gudgeons, that they are a spontaneous product of pond mud, that they are hermaphrodites and fertilize themselves, and so on. Among these fictions there comes to light from time to time what animal physiologists term a "legitimate mistake"—one based on the results of a reasonable conjecture. Thus the conscientious ichthyologist E. Blanchard surmised that the eels we catch in our streams are no more than the larvae of an unknown adult form, living in this state for a long period and finally acquiring an apparently definitive aspect, except as regards the mature development of the sexual organs— rather as the axolotl is the larva of the Amblystoma, although capable quite exceptionally of breeding and reproducing itself.

Meanwhile certain small fish, flat and transparent, and shaped like willow leaves, were being caught in the sea by fishermen, and studied in the laboratories by naturalists who classified them under the name "Leptocephalae." No one thought to attribute to them even the slightest relationship with eels.

Now, to waste no more time over these eras of uncertainty, let us come straight to recent discoveries, with which, more than any other, the name of the Danish scientist J. Schmidt is associated, and which earned him his fame.

The eels that we have seen in the upper reaches of rivers, or in standing water, are in the very great majority young females waiting the necessary time—a matter of several years—for their mature development. Sometimes this development is delayed, or is even unable to occur—for instance, in aquaria. Then the eel, sedentary all the time, becomes enormous, and one day brings unexpected joy to an angler who, in his subsequent accounts of it, can only describe its size by comparing it with his own arm, then, a little later, with the calf of his leg, and finally, if no one stops him, with his thigh.

Normally, when the female eels are about a yard to a yard and a half long, they take on a beautiful orange color with silvery glints; their eyes enlarge; and, no longer eating, they start during autumn to come down the rivers, in groups packed so closely that the stream sometimes rolls numbers of them into tangles. In the estuaries they once more meet the young male eels, who are also afflicted by the same feverish desire to get away. Then all the eels make for the sea and are lost to sight.

Today, we know where they go, but this knowledge is no less productive of enigmas than is ignorance, since the eels—all of them, whether from Norway or Spain, Morocco or Iceland, the Baltic or the Mediterranean, to say nothing of the east coast of America—make for the same region of the Atlantic, the center of which, not far from Bermuda, can be given roughly as 25° N. 55° W. In fact, it is in that Sargasso Sea which was so long a mystery and a source of terror to old-time navigators.

We can follow them thus far, but once they get here we do not know what becomes of them, from the moment when, after laying or fertilizing their eggs, they disappear into the depths, just as the salmon disappeared. The salmon, however, were seen to return; but we never see the return of the eels. And so, from this point onward, our study must concern itself with the eggs and their fate.

In the warm water, and among the masses of floating weed that characterize the region, these eggs hatch out. The fry emerging from them are not the elvers we might expect, but are certainly Leptocephalae, which, formerly classified as a separate species, as we have seen, are in fact the larvae of eels. But so little do they resemble the creature they will eventually become that we would never guess their identity had we not seen them make the transformation.

Moreover, they take plenty of time over deciding, and for several years they remain Leptocephalae while they drift slowly toward our shores. Millions are lost by depredation, but, innumerable as ever, they end by becoming elvers as soon as they reach the continental plateau and the vicinity of the estuaries. Soon after, in their new form, and in the winter or the spring, they undertake the ascent of the rivers.

Thus the migration of eels is the direct opposite of that of salmon, which, hatched in the river, go down to the sea in order to mature, then return to breed at the place of origin. Eels, on the other hand, born in the sea, ascend the rivers to take on their adult shape, and return to their deep-sea starting point to lay and fertilize their eggs. A similar fatal and implacable force drives both species towards their goals, directing and controlling them, then deserting and sacrificing them, once their mission has been fulfilled. And this has gone on for hundreds of millions of years.

## Catadromes and Anadromes

These are not the specific names of rare fish, but two terms used to describe, either species that, like the eels, lay their eggs in the sea, or those, such as the salmon, that lay their eggs in fresh water.

The gray mullet, sea bream, bass and so on belong to the first group. We know them all, and even those of us least given to fishing have seen shoals of gray mullet, sometimes in huge numbers, foraging offshore where a river meets the sea, and leaping above the brackish surface in the search for food. Sometimes, too, we see them at sea, for the whole length of a beach; and at other times, far up rivers in fresh water. In short, the estuary is their normal habitat, and it is only the breeding fish that generally at the start of autumn descend into salt water—never very far—in order to lay their eggs; and it is chiefly the young fish that, at the beginning of spring, ascend the rivers and come to fresh water.

Thus among this group we find the eels' habits reproduced in miniature, so to speak, with migration reduced to simple displacements of small extent, which provides us with a chance to study them from start to finish—a great advantage.

The sea bream (genus *Chrysophrys*) is equally familiar to us. It is common in the Mediterranean, and its gastronomic fame can be traced from Roman times. Indeed, the famous bream of the Lucrine Lake have a special place in Roman history.

Taken as a whole, the sea bream's habits are analogous to those of the gray mullet, and very nearly the same goes for the bass, which, incidentally, has a gastronomic value equal, if not superior, to the others.

Among the anadromes—those fish analogous to the salmon in their breeding habits—first place must be given to trout, interesting in that some of them never leave fresh water, others only pass from still water to running water to lay their eggs, and still others go down to the sea to develop and mature, yet never stray far from the shore. Trout are equally interesting in that they offer an easy-to-study epitome of the salmons' habits.

Trout, in spite of their maritime sojourns, remain primarily river fish. On the other hand, shad, which also enter fresh water for breeding purposes, are, taking their lives as a whole, sea fish, and it is to the sea that their fry, in the first few months, hasten to return; even the breeding fish never go very far upstream before depositing their eggs. Moreover, these species form part of a family, Clupeidae, whose principal members—herrings, anchovies and sardines —are extremely sensitive to the slightest variation of salinity.

Among the anadromes the sturgeon and the lamprey should be mentioned, the first for its enormous size (some specimens are said to have exceeded 19 feet and weighed more than 2,000 pounds), and its roe, from which caviar is made, the females laying as many as five or six million eggs at a time; and the lamprey for its round, suctorial mouth, with no jawbone supporting it, and for the elementary structure of its skeleton, which places it in the lowest ranks of the vertebrates.

### *Seasonal Migrants*

Finally, there is a third group to be examined, one that could, in truth, include almost all fish—by stretching a point or two—but which we will limit to the chief examples of those fish whose migrations are the most evident and extensive, and which are limited exclusively to salt water.

Of these, the prime example is the tuna.

In contrast to the lamprey, the tuna appears to occupy an elevated rank among the vertebrates, since it presents certain characteristics found only in the higher vertebrates. For instance, its blood temperature is notably higher than that of the water in which it evolves; and everyone knows its rich, firm flesh, slightly reminiscent of the meat of herbivorous mammals. The pickled flesh of the white tuna is comparable to veal, while the red tuna, fresh, and excellent in that state, is rather like beef, although nowadays we seldom encounter it except in fishing ports.

Several species of tuna frequent our shores. We will confine ourselves to the two principal kinds: the common or red tuna (*Orcynus thynnus*), which is caught mainly in the Mediterranean, and the albacore, or white tuna (*Germo alalunga*), which, commoner in the Atlantic, is above all recognizable by its long, pectoral fin, shaped like a scythe blade.

These are magnificent fish: the red tuna may be 26 feet long and weigh some 650 pounds, while its powerful muscular system and compact belly provide a streamlined shape that can dart through the water like a torpedo.

Although the tuna has been caught for food since remotest antiquity, bringing a fortune to Byzantium—"It is thought," says Coutière, "that Istanbul's famous Golden Horn owes its name to the enormous profits accruing from this fish at the times of its migration"—and although all its movements have been followed and studied with close attention, its habits and migrations have nevertheless been the object of vague and contradictory theories right down to our own times.

As regards the Atlantic, we know that tuna appear in great numbers in the Gulf of Cadiz toward the end of April, and in the Mediterranean, on the southeast coast of Spain, around Sardinia and Sicily, and off Tunisia. They can then be seen swimming in large shoals not far from the shore, always heading in the same direction, a circumstance that allows the tuna fishermen to wait for them and trap them in kettle nets installed athwart their route. Until the end of June they are caught in thousands.

Meanwhile, on the French coast, for instance, virtually

not a single tuna will be found. In July, however, this is where they appear, in bloodthirsty pursuit of anchovies and sardines. They soon show themselves in huge shoals in some fortunate areas such as the Gulf of Lions, where they remain throughout the fine weather, departing with the advent of inclement weather. In March and April there is no longer one to be seen.

In the Atlantic—thanks principally to the efforts of R. Legendre—the albacore has been subjected to comparable studies. They appear off Morocco in the spring, then, during May, ascend the length of Portugal, entering the Bay of Biscay at the end of the month. It is then that the fishing starts, no longer with the aid of kettle nets, but, at this much greater distance from the shore, by means of lines, and from boats specially equipped for the purpose, vessels for which the familiar tuna boats of Concarneau are the model.

Little by little the fish and the fishermen disperse northward, toward the open sea, until, in September, they reach the south-west of Iceland; and in the early days of October the tuna boats make their return. The fish have vanished. The campaign is over. Sometimes, when things have been good, there have been some marvelous catches, as many as 100,000 fish caught in a single day! Here let us note a detail important for our inquiry: tuna are never caught by night.

Needless to say, a great number of other species have been the subject of similar studies, sometimes giving rise to theories long held to be self-evident and irrefutable.

In the last century, for instance, countless observers had the herring undertaking gigantic circuits, the exact courses of which were traced. Then reaction set in, and it was decided that the herring made no lateral migrations whatsoever, only vertical ones.

To be fair, we must recognize that despite the very great progress made in this field, a considerable number of points still remain to be elucidated. Nevertheless today we know that the herring comprise a number of different breeds, each occupying a given area—such as the North Sea or the Baltic—where they only make relatively slight migratory displacements, for reasons we will explain presently.

Migratory fish of this kind or comparable—seasonal migrants, that is—include mackerel, sardines, anchovies, cod, whiting, haddock and many others. We can only name the best known, without dwelling on their biological aspects.

Now for the explanations.

### Interpreting the Facts

Several general theories relating to migration suggest themselves as applying to the fish mentioned above, but we shall have to review them in the context of our whole survey. For the moment let us summarize—very briefly, of necessity—only those that concern our fish.

Salmon, as L. Roule points out, only lay their eggs in water with a high oxygen content—at least seven to eight cubic centimeters to the liter. These conditions are found near river sources, and to reach these areas the salmon lets nothing stand in its way. Thus we see it swimming upstream against strong currents, and leaping obstacles several meters high. It is urged onward by what is known as a *tropism*—a tendency determined by the influence of the external environment, unconscious, independent of the will, predestined and as ineluctable as the force that turns a flower to the sun, or thrusts a root deep into the ground.

The oxygen stimulates the development of the alevins from the eggs. But there comes a time, after they attain maturity and have undergone a thorough transformation, when they become subject to a new tropism, this time a negative one, which is dependent on the action of light rays.

Before the alevin undertakes its downstream excursion, its tissues are provided with a pigment that acts as a protective screen against light. When the pigmentary changes "destroy this screen, the young salmon finds itself unprotected, and it seeks the deepest water, where the light rays have a diminished effect. Then it lets itself drift away from the hatching grounds, where the water is shallow and the daylight strong. Presently it gains the main stream of the river, and finally it reaches the sea. Thus its descent is the result of a phototropism of a negative type. . . ."

The eel is also influenced by tropisms, but of another sort. Here temperature comes into play: the exodus takes place in autumn, at which season the inland waters grow cold more quickly and more markedly than the sea. With eels, "From start to finish their descent of the river and departure into the sea has the effect of guiding them toward those places where the summer temperature is best conserved, and away from those places where the winter temperature is already making itself felt." This phenomenon is one of thermotropism.

As for the elvers' migration in the opposite direction,

they are subjected to another influence—that of branchio-tropism, i.e., the needs of their respiratory systems produce a similar effect to the one we have seen acting on the salmon.

We have had to reduce this theory to its simplest outlines, and it is one that has already been criticized as being too inflexible. However, a fuller exposition would not avoid the criticism, and we shall review some of the serious objections in our conclusion. Here let us deal only with those that bear directly on our present subject.

It is astonishing to see with what unfaltering perfection these tropisms work.

For instance, does the young salmon, in its journey from the place where it is born to the seabed where it achieves maturity, have to follow an incontrovertible route marked by an ever-increasing darkness, as a stone must roll down a sloping groove? And does the eel become progressively warmer from its starting point in some French pond or Spanish lake until it reaches the Sargasso Sea? And what new tropism, inserted into its itinerary, guides it when it crosses dry land to get from one body of water to another? Or, again, what other tropism is it that influences the salmon not to stop when it comes to a waterfall—which might well detain it, since the water there is probably more oxygenated than that at the source—but, instead, to leap it with a bound into pure air, which should certainly interrupt, or virtually destroy, the tropism's effect?

And so on. Rather than dwell on these questions, let us seek an answer.

Now, although apprehensive as always of travestying

an author's argument by condensing it into too short an outline, we will deal briefly with a thesis that, while taking account of tropisms—and they must be taken account of—introduces other elements, which allow us to come to closer grips with the problems.

E. Le Danois, in some admirable oceanographic studies, has shown that the oceans are subject to alternate movements of advance and retreat, movements that can be described as the sea's *diastole* and *systole,* or again, as a sort of respiratory rhythm, causing the expansion of one area of water in relation to another, or its contraction.

The extent and periodicity of these movements are not precisely determinable, since they depend on a variety of cosmic causes. Some coincide with the seasons, others with infinitely longer intervals; and similar extreme variations are encountered as regards their extent and importance.

For the moment it is enough for us to know that this rhythmic effect is due to the essential difference between the polar waters, cold, heavy, placid and inert, clinging to the continental profile to form a casing around the emergent land; and the tropical waters, light and active which "represent the living part of the ocean, one that struggles ceaselessly against the inertia of the other part, and whose waters insinuate themselves into the polar waters when they can as if from a need to encroach upon them."

For another thing, we know that the distribution of land and water over the globe's surface was not always as it is now. Notably, before the sea's action and other causes had their effect, there was a time when the regions that are now France, England, Ireland and Germany were not separated by any sea, but had a common coastline, extending certainly as far west as Brittany and as far north as the Shetlands. Amongst the areas enclosed was the Dogger Bank plateau, now a famous fishing ground, where the trawls sometimes catch the bones of elephants and rhinoceroses along with the fish.

The rivers that flow through these countries today were much longer, running down to those coasts that are now beneath the sea. The Rhine—swollen by the waters of the Elbe, the Somme, the Thames, the Tweed and the Tay—had its mouth near the 56th parallel, between Scotland and Norway. The Seine, having as tributaries the Orne, the Vire, the Rance and the Elorn, as well as the Hampshire Avon, met the sea far beyond what is now Cape Ushant. The Severn, with the Mersey and the rivers of Ireland for tributaries, had its estuary some hundred and fifty miles beyond Land's End.

To return to our fish, Le Danois, speaking of the salmon, tells us that "all catches of salmon made by trawlers in deep water can be assigned to the sites of the estuaries and deltas of the vanished rivers."

This statement throws a vivid light on the problem. The tropisms—if they exist—that determine the migrants' journey are at all events indicated by clear signposts, so to speak, and this goes far toward explaining the creatures' behavior.

"The fish, swimming deeper and deeper, follows the course of the main river as far as the place where the ancient watercourse had its estuary on the edge of the continental plateau, and where the channel of its outfall became lost among the mud shelves . . . there the salmon spends its marine life, feeding itself copiously."

On the return journey, the same route is followed. "Thus the salmon's fidelity to its native stream is very easily explained. In fact, the salmon has no trouble at all in finding the river's channel again, since it has never left it."

Still quoting the same author, the leptocephals' migration "is quite inexplicable unless reference is made to the movements of the water mass. Indeed, the larvae's distribution shows that the concentric zones where they are found according to their age and size do not correspond at all to the flow of the ocean currents, and in some places the movement is even in the opposite direction to the current; thus it must be the whole oceanic mass containing leptocephals that undergoes displacement, transporting the larvae in its midst from the Sargasso Sea to Europe and Africa. The leptocephals are carried along by the corporate movement of the water. . . ."

Le Danois gives us some concise observations on the biology of seasonal fish, one of which will serve as an example:

"The sea frequented by the albacore off the coasts of Europe has a temperature exceeding 14° C. at twenty-seven fathoms, and the fish's biology is wholly governed by this fact. It achieves its migratory dispersion by following the water's corporative movements, always moving within these limits and following their outlines in every detail. . . ." On its return "the albacore, aligning itself to the same limits, descends into deep water, always in the midst of the water mass," which gradually carries it downward. For a similar reason, the albacore is never caught at night, since it is then that it goes down into deeper water—still, however, limited by a water temperature of 14° C.—to catch the semi-abyssal species that form its prey.

So, concludes Le Danois, "waters with a temperature of 14° C. or over constitute the albacore's habitat throughout its life. It follows these waters on the surface during its dispersal migration, and it accompanies them to the depths at the time of its breeding migration."

Similar determining factors explain the comings and goings of other species.

Thus the herring is governed by the water's salinity, and it obeys the corporate movement of its marine habitat by keeping within its limits. To the degree that the water of the Atlantic advances or recedes, the herring retreats from it or follows it, without ever entering it.

Moreover it should be noted that herring concentrate in certain areas to mature sexually, and later, resort to another region to lay their eggs. This represents an atavistic memory of the fishes' former anadromous habits. "The points at which they concentrate before maturing correspond to the channels and estuaries of the great prehistoric rivers."

Conversely, mackerel are arrested by the outfall of the inland waters, which prevents them from leaving sea water. Lastly, a simpler theory still suggests that fish, not to mention other animals, possess a "homing instinct" that, unrecognizable to us, leads them where they should go.

## 3 / The Migrations of Mammals

A strictly systematic approach would now lead us to study birds, but birds are such accomplished migrants that we shall leave them till last.

Moreover we shall have nothing to say about amphibians and reptiles. Almost all of them hibernate, and consequently they are sedentary creatures, faithful to the place where the summer temperature suits them. No doubt toads and frogs make changes in their habitat as they colonize their neighborhood, or are even carried considerable distances by turbulent air conditions; and the gecko, following in man's footsteps, is an almost involuntary migrant. Also, we know that some snakes—rattlesnakes, for instance—resort *en masse* to certain places where they spend the winter, the choice quite often falling upon human dwellings, which is not much appreciated by the rightful occupant. However, these movements, and others like them, are accidental and of minimal importance. We shall ignore them.

As we said at the outset, the most usual cause of animal migration is the search for food, whether it be a case of herbivores seeking new pastures, or carnivores following them.

We need not cite every example, and instances will be found among all the orders of the class. Some we shall refer to only in passing; others, which present details that depart from the norm, we shall dwell on at greater length.

In short, some, such as the cetaceans (whales and others) and the pinnipeds (seals, seal lions and walruses) deserve separate study because of their habitat, while others, such as the chiropters (bats), deserve it because of their physiology.

### The Trails of the Bison

We shall deliberately set aside the lowest orders of mammals, which are confined to their respective territories —monotremes, marsupials and edentates—in order to come at once to the ungulates (hoofed animals). As regards these, popular literature forestalled the naturalists' efforts—most successfully, in the public's estimation—by describing one particular migratory species that today interests us both because it is now almost extinct in the regions that were its original habitat, and because of a certain atmosphere of tragedy surrounding its eclipse.

We mean, of course, the American bison, or buffalo. Chateaubriand drew attention to this animal, with that slightly comic emphasis which is the penalty paid by genius for the misuse of its gifts.

The scene is the valleys of the "Meschacebé," and he

describes for us the departure of a herd of bison under its leader's guidance when the dictates of Providence inform it that the time is ripe:

"When the moment comes, the leader, shaking his mane, which hangs everywhere about his eyes and curving horns, salutes the setting sun, lowering his head and raising his back mountainously; at the same time, a dull bellow, the signal for departure, escapes from his deep chest, then suddenly he plunges into the foaming waves, followed by the host of bulls and heifers bellowing their devotion in his wake."

When the Europeans arrived, the bison were scattered across the North American continent over an area that can be roughly contained by a line drawn some three hundred miles south of the Mexican border, running up through Nevada, Oregon and Alberta as far as the Great Slave Lake, then following the shores of Hudson Bay, until in the end it touches the Atlantic coast below Boston—the ocean, together with the Appalachian Mountains, forming this vast region's eastern limit, outside of which it seems that only Florida—anyway, present-day Florida—should be placed.

In a word, a good third of the land area was inhabited by this magnificent beast, so distinct from related species by virtue of its humped withers, its huge, heavy head with its tangled beard and mane, its wide nostrils, the shortness of its neck, its powerful forequarters, its woolly coat and its horns so short as to be almost lost in the thickness of its fleece.

It is recorded that until the nineteenth century the

number of bison was so great "that no other species of mammal, it is believed, has ever reached it" (Ménégaux). But doubtless this assertion is exaggerated, even if we do not count the proliferations of certain rodents and other small animals: in the bison's own family, the Bovidae, there must exist, notably among various of the African antelopes, still larger herds.

Nonetheless it remains true that the bison's numerical strength was important to a degree that we can hardly conceive. Although no reliable statistics were ever compiled when it was still possible, the figures put out by the various authors who deal with the problem are certainly contestable, and quite sincere observers seem sometimes to have been shaky in their arithmetic to the point of thinking that the number of zeros on the number's right had no significance. Thus, in 1866, General Sheridan, finding himself in the presence of an immense herd moving slowing past under his gaze, concluded, with the help of his staff, that it comprised some ten million beasts! Later, he admitted to himself that "it wouldn't do"!

Martin S. Garretson, of New York's Bronx Zoo, has written a work about the American bison that probably brings us much closer to the truth by estimating their total number at some sixty millions. "This calculation seems fantastic," he adds, "but the figure can be accepted if we take certain facts into consideration and bear in mind the vastness of the area where these animals lived."*

* Martin S. Garretson, *The American Bison* (New York: New York Zoological Society).

We accept his figure, then, and for the rest, it is only important for us to remember that the bison were extremely numerous, and that this abundance partly explains the need for their migrations.

Usually they lived in great herds, but to a considerable extent these were split up into small groups—into families, it is believed—that grazed on the immense plains, where they sought various grasses, including that buffalo grass (*Buchloe dactyloides*) which propagates by means of stolons, and which today has itself almost entirely disappeared from its chosen areas before the advance of human cultivation.

To chew the cud the bison lay down with their feet hidden beneath their bodies (to protect them from the attacks of insects), and with their muzzles always to windward. At the slightest alarm they jumped up, getting to their feet with a promptness unknown in domestic cattle, and the herd at once closed its ranks, governed by that gregarious instinct that is a characteristic of the breed, and that shows itself at the least provocation.

In the summer pastures, they were wont to scoop out dust bowls of a sort, and they loved rolling in the powdery dirt. Even today, one comes upon a good many of these hollows, often transformed into water holes; and in the old days, the frontier scouts were happy to use them as trenches in their fights with the Indians.

If a rock or a tree was to be found in the vicinity, the bison used it as a rubbing post, and rocks can still be seen polished to the smoothness of glass. Later on, the bison put telegraph poles to the same use. Iron spikes were driven into the poles to keep them at a distance, but they at once developed a preference for these spiked nails, which scratched better.

If the need for food is one explanation of the bison's journeys, it is not the only one.

Some pastures were abandoned, when the supplies of fodder were still plentiful, for others that, to human eyes, seemed in no way more advantageous. Similarly, changes in temperature cannot always be given as an explanation. Many herds wintered in the snow, sometimes perishing in it, when it would have been easy for them to find a milder climate elsewhere. On the other hand, in the northern territories there were regular autumnal migrations, not toward the south, as one might expect, but toward the west. There it was at least as cold at the foot of the ranges, although the mountains provided a protective screen against the winds that blow in winter from the Pacific. Elsewhere, it was certainly warmth and rich pastures that the herd went in search of.

It was not possible to study these migrations with as much precision as could be desired. By the time naturalists became seriously occupied by the problem, the emigrants, by blazing the trails that took them into the Far West, had already profoundly changed the bison's habits, dividing the species' total strength into several groups, some of which ceased migrating to the south, while others no longer returned to the north. Some herds, for instance, were confined to Pennsylvania, never leaving it, although formerly they had been in the habit of migrating as far as Kentucky and beyond.

Nevertheless, in spite of everything, the majority of the great trails have been identified—here and there evidence of them is found even today—thanks to the astonishingly regular habits of the animals that made use of them, and to the persistence of tracks that can be traced undeviatingly after countless centuries.

"The world," says Garretson again, "has never known better natural engineers than the bison, since they invariably chose the line of least resistance and knew how to give their trails the best section that a professional engineer could calculate. The surveyors charged with plotting the railway's track across the plains adopted the bison's ancient trail for a considerable distance without being able to improve on its section. The Baltimore and Ohio Railroad followed the route of the great ruminants for the mountain crossing as far as the Ohio River, and the Union Pacific did the same when it built its line between Omaha and the Rocky Mountains."

Indeed, the bison crossed mountains with an agility surprising in such massive creatures, sometimes boasting a ton of flesh.* Certain cliffs that still bear traces of the bison's regular passage cannot be scaled by men using their hands and feet.

In places where the bison moved along the mountain-

* A bull was killed in Texas that weighed 3,000 pounds. The average is 1,750 pounds for the males, and 1,300 to 1,500 pounds for the females.

side laterally, instead of leaping from slope to slope, the parallel trails formed terraces looking like infinitely long flights of steps, each about a yard above the next and a foot wide, along which the animals filed in close order. Even today, ridges of the most green and lush grass mark the mountainside trails, and that it grows so strongly is due, in all likelihood, to the churning up of the soil by the bison's hooves, and to a superabundant fertilization with animal manure through countless millennia.

When the herd was on the move it did not form a single mass, but was composed of droves, each averaging some ten thousand head, following on at short intervals, and all witnesses agree that, despite the extensive horizons, the plain was covered as far as the eye could see. Trustworthy observers, encountering one of these herds in Arkansas, estimated that it comprised more than four million head. They asserted that the main body moved past uninterruptedly for several days, covering an area of 1,250 square miles.

The order in which these immense armies advanced was not left to chance. The cows and their calves occupied the center, and were flanked by the bulls, who guarded them. The oldest males brought up the rear—perhaps because they had no choice—while lame and ailing animals trailed far to the rear, closely followed by wolves and coyotes, which, not daring to attack the main body, generally solid in defense, showed no mercy to the stragglers. In this way natural selection came into play, and this, far from harming the species, encouraged its prosperity, by letting the fittest survive, and by stamping out epidemic contagion, which today, in spite of human care, all too frequently decimates the herds on the reserves, the breed's sole survivors.

Nothing stopped the herd on the move; and contrary to an opinion too often expressed, the force that drove it forward was not always prescient by virtue of instinct's infallible wisdom, since more than once catastrophe intervened.

One such catastrophe occurred in 1867 on the South Platte River in Colorado, when the leading echelons, entering the shallow water, stirred up the muddy bottom in a morass of quicksand that engulfed thousands of beasts while those behind continued to press forward.

Or it might be the ice of a late winter that broke beneath their weight, drowning them in droves without once halting those that followed. A downstream witness of one such debacle tried to count the floating corpses. He stopped, discouraged, when 7,360 had floated by. And the procession continued for three days.

On yet another occasion the herd was surprised by a snow storm of which instinct had given no warning. As was their custom, they advanced into it head-on, and the leaders, blinded by the blizzard, came to the edge of a sheer precipice too late to stop themselves. The herd following them pushed them over, and its was estimated that this disaster destroyed 100,000 bison, whose bones lay for many years along the entire length of the cliff foot to a depth of some thirty feet.

Periods of drought also took heavy toll of the bison's numbers. And finally, contemporaries have left us some sad accounts of the tragedies resulting from prairie fires. The unfortunate beasts would be trapped, despite the urgency of their stampede, and even this plight was surpassed in those that did not die in the fire, but, appallingly injured, blinded, tortured by burns, consumed by unquenchable thirst, only perished miserably after prolonged agony.

Nevertheless, as we have said, the herd was in fine fettle when the white man began to realize that there was money to be made from it.

It did not last long. By November, 1883, it was thought that there was no longer a single wild bison in the whole of America, following the massacre of the last herd in North Dakota. However, in 1889, a small scattered herd was discovered in the Red Desert of Wyoming. It consisted of some thirty head, and it was wiped out as soon as seen.

These were probably the last representatives of a species that, less than fifty years before, had numbered many tens of millions.

## *The Antelopes' Circuits*

The first travelers to visit South Africa delighted in describing their wonder at the countless herds of antelopes they met with, and they left us some observations on the habits of these graceful animals that their successors could do no more than confirm, until their admiration became tedious by repetition.

The species that their writings were concerned with more than any was the springbok, which name was given it by the Dutch settlers. This is the *Gazella euchore* of the naturalists, remarkable for its pretty, twisted horns, with their lyre-shaped formation, its tawny-brown coat, its white belly, its white face with brown stripes, and the white line that runs along its back.

It was by the millions that these animals assembled on the vast desert plains of southern Africa, where they stayed, not only throughout the rainy season, but also into the dry season as long as the last waterhole did not dry up, or the last grass wither, which did not happen every year. Otherwise, they made their way toward the south, moving from pasture to pasture until they came to the mountains. Then, turning at the foot of the range, they made they way back across other plains, until eventually they were back at their point of departure, to which, meanwhile, the rains had returned, reviving the pastures and replenishing the drinking holes. This journey of some thousands of miles took almost a year.

"All those who have seen, as I have, the infinite number of these migrants," says Gordon Cumming, "and truthfully relates what he has seen, must fear disbelief. These herds are something so extraordinary that they can best be compared to locusts' swarms. Like locusts, they cause all vegetation to disappear in a few hours, and destroy a settlement's every crop in a single night.

"It was on December 28th that I first had the pleasure of witnessing one of these migrations. Two hours before dawn I was roused from my wagon by the antelopes' bleating. I supposed that a herd was grazing within a couple of hundred yards of the camp, but when day broke I saw that the whole plain was literally covered with these animals. They approached slowly from the west, pouring from between two hills like a river, eventually disappearing behind some heights a mile to the northeast . . .

"Enormous though this herd was, that same evening I saw another even more numerous descending from between the hills as had the first ones. The whole plain and even the slopes of the hills appeared to be covered by a single mass of these animals, monopolising the view as far as the eye could see. It would be hopeless to try to estimate their number, but I believe I can say that several hundreds of thousands were within sight all at the same time."

Accounts by a number of witnesses can only repeat the same facts, but some have picturesque details to add.

Thus Wood speaks of an occasion when a flock of sheep were swamped by one of these herds, and were swept along with it, unable to get away; and the Boer settlers seriously affirm that a similar misadventure once overtook some lions! A little reflection suggests that this is not an impossibility. It is clear that nothing can oppose the force of numbers, and the thrust of some hundreds of thousands of bodies, fragile though each may be in itself, is irresistible. One cannot repel a tide.

Nevertheless, when the lions manage to avoid such humiliating experiences, they find opportunity in these troops of meat for enormous banquets. They follow the herds in bands, gorging themselves on the food, and the panthers do the same, to the peril of the enfeebled and the stragglers. Then come the jackals, sharing what is left of the lions' meal; and the last of the carrion is for the hyenas, *tarde venientibus.* As for the the vultures, they range over the whole region, and know very well how to get their share.

Here again natural selection plays a part, to the general benefit. While the leading antelopes, well-fed and secure, graze lazily, those toward the rear of the herd, hard-pressed by beasts of prey, and finding nothing to eat on a terrain sterilized as by fire, redouble their efforts to get to the front and end by succeeding, thus insuring a perpetual rotation that maintains equity and, by and large, guarantees the common interests.

If these gazelles are remarkable for their vast numbers —now considerably diminished—they are far from being the only ones to undertake migrations of this sort. And here we have done no more than select one example from a great many, and by no means a special case.

In principle, almost all the grass-eaters make journeys, and usually the reason that urges them to leave their customary habitats is so evident that there would no real need to dwell upon it, if there were not sometimes observed in closely related groups deviations from normal habits that simply cannot be explained solely by the necessity to change either pastures or drinking holes. Here again we must content ourselves with just one example, taken almost at random.

Thus the oryx, true nomads, go north with the coming of the first rains and return south during March, when the hot weather starts. Here man is of direct assistance to us in studying this animal, since, as In Tanoust tells us: "When the nomadic shepherds move north at the start of the winter season, the oryx go ahead of them—at some distance; and when the shepherds come south in the dry season, the oryx follow them—again at a distance." Clearly this is not a matter simply of grass and water.

The migrations of the addax, belonging to the same sub-family, extend even further, taking place between the Sahara and the Sahel region of Upper Senegal with a very regular incidence. Furthermore, in years of extreme drought these animals are driven to take bold measures, reaching areas where they are virtually unknown at other times.

Yet the kudu (*Strepsiceros strepsiceros* Pocock), a closely related group and the magnificent possessors of the trophy—their long, spiral horns—most sought after by African hunters, never, as far as we know, leave their mountainous habitat, in some places, while in others they go down freely to the plains, even when there is no lack of water in their normal locality. It is said that the mountain-dwellers are able to drink throughout the day, thanks to various aqueous fruits—watermelons and others—found in their areas, while the addax have even less need for water. (Some authors go so far as to maintain that they never drink, but no doubt this is an exaggeration.) In any case, their abstemiousness does not keep them from making regular migrations, even though not beset by absolute necessity.

Nevertheless we repeat that necessity is the chief factor governing herbivores, and is what principally influences them, whether antelopes or cattle, elephants or members of the pig family, deer or horses,* or even an example of that apparently most indolent feeder, the hippopotamus—that is, if we can consider as migrations "those changes of residence that each year, in July or August, take it from the big rivers that are its habitat in the dry season, to the tributaries or to the water holes of the interior" (Malbrant).

On the other hand, the giraffes, in all likelihood, would be willingly sedentary if their timidity and their predatory enemies did not oblige them to move from place to place, although on no regular pattern. However, the rhinoceros can be considered truly sedentary, and so can its "anatomical relative," the hyrax.

## Forced Migrants

Only a few words need be said concerning the carnivores, since they can hardly be included among migratory animals, even when, as we have just seen, they keep on the trail of their prey.

Indeed, we must point out that it is not the same carnivores that follow the herd from one end of the journey to the other; this was easy to see as regards the bison, where

* There are virtually no more true wild horses in existence, but the dziggetai (*Equus Hemionus*) and their related species clearly have nomadic habits. As for the Cervidae, all more or less nomadic, they, with the reindeer—and especially its American variety, the caribou— present a migratory type almost comparable in importance of journeys and vast size of herds to those we have chosen as the most representative, the bison and the antelope.

To mention another instance, this time nearer home, everyone has heard of those strange periodic migrations of wild boar, which arrive in France from time to time in considerable numbers from the forests of Eastern Europe.

the species of wolf attacking them differed according to the territory they crossed. Nevertheless, in the absence of a controlling factor, it is known that the large carnivores, such as lions, do not tolerate the intrusion of rival families on their territory, and are forced, more or less, to respect that of their neighbors. Moreover, in other places, when its prey migrates during the dry season, the lion—and others of the large felines—rather than follow it, turns upon the resident game, and this is when it is most dangerous.

In some places, certain years see the appearance of quantities of various small carnivores—rare until then—which are quickly reduced until their numbers revert to normal. But here again their migrations are strictly dependent on those of their own prey.

One of the most curious examples of this dependence is that of the Canadian lynx on the white hare, both denizens of the same areas, a phenomenon that recurs at almost ten-year intervals.

The rhythm is as follows: In a given period the hares proliferate, thanks to the species' fertility. The lynx descend upon them from all parts to profit from the windfall. Yet it is not then that they are at their most numerous. At the outset, stimulated by plentiful food, they mate and bring into the world numbers of cubs, which they rear with ease. Just when the lynx's numerical strength is at its maximum the hares, already decimated by their enemies, are periodically attacked by an epidemic that shows itself by a swelling of the throat and by sores on the joints, and that kills them off by the thousand. When the hares have all perished the lynx are still plentiful, but gradually life becomes impossible for them. Those that can, migrate, and the others succumb miserably one by one. In the lean years, trappers only come upon the occasional lynx by chance, gaunt and starving, its pelt worthless, and this in the very places where, four or five years before, healthy lynxes could have been caught at will, and where the trappers know they will again catch them four or five years hence.

Animal associations of this sort, where the life of one species depends upon another's, are not rare. We have seen them existing between wolves and cattle, lions and antelopes, with advantage to the herd when the beast of prey is unsuccessful; and it can be found between many other species, from the tiger, battening upon boars or peafowl, down to stoats and weasels preying upon small rodents.

Appropriately, it is the small rodents that next engage our attention.

## *One-Way Migrations*

The example we cite is no more than a representative type, chosen from a number as seeming the most perfect of its kind. But if we speak only of this one, this does not mean that it is an exception. Far to the contrary. Let us say, referring to a comment made in our opening pages, that the animal in question is to rodents what the swallow is to birds: a popular symbol for a migrant. But it has more than one related species that imitates it.

The Norwegian lemming, *Myodes lemmus*, with its compact body, very short tail and paws designed for digging, is related to the water-vole of our latitudes. It is rather larger in size, reaching some six or seven inches, and like the vole, it is endowed with formidable fertility.

It is found to a small extent everywhere in the Arctic zone, and due to its presence in Norway, has been observed and described since quite early times. Its natural history was deemed worthy of a place in the records of scientists from the beginning of the sixteenth century, and as it is rather extraordinary, its legend was not slow to take hold, and with embellishments.

Thus it was related that the lemmings were born in the clouds and, as numerous as raindrops, fell to earth in showers. Grass that they touched killed cattle; and later, Buffon himself, hearing of this, was to affirm that in the end they destroyed themselves by hanging themselves from boughs, or by hurling themselves into water.

Already, in his time, however, the species' habits had been studied by Linnaeus, to such good purpose that there are only a few details to add to his study. Here we will only mention those that relate to the animal's migration.

After a period of normal existence that can last ten, fifteen or twenty years, or even longer, during which the lemmings show themselves as no more remarkable than any other small mammal, they are all at once seen to assemble in numbers beyond counting, especially in mountainous regions. They then soon move off in massed columns, always advancing in a direct line, and from then on no obstacle of any sort can stop them.

A stream, or a river, and they do not even hesitate. They throw themselves into it and cross it. It does not matter if several drown during the crossing, for there are always more that reach the other side. In any case, they do not spare themselves hardship, and, for instance, will swim a lake at its widest part if that part happens to lie on the line of march toward their goal; their motto seems to be "Straight on, straight on, forever." If the obstacle that lies in their path is vulnerable to their claws, they tunnel under it; if it is an impregnable rock, they go around it, but resume the straight line of their advance as soon as they reach its further face. If it is a boat that they encounter, they do not swim around it, but swarm over it, plunging into the water on its other side. Their numbers are sometimes so countless that, at the time of the 1823 migration studied by Zetter-stedt, several loaded boats barely avoided foundering.

Where do they go? No one knows. Or, at least, no one knows where they would go if they were free to get to the end of their trail. But in regions where they can be followed their migration ends fatally in the sea, and they get there so depleted that all trace of them is lost. In fact, as they make their way seaward, they are prey to such an onslaught of appetites that gradually their numbers dwindle like water on sand. It is not the largest enemies that take the greatest toll, and stoats alone are responsible for the best part of the slaughter, helped, however, by everything that eats flesh, whether habitually or occasionally. Weasels, martens, sables, foxes and wolverines throw themselves on the quarry, and wolves and bears themselves seize their share. Then all the birds of prey, especially the nocturnal ones, headed by the monstrous hawk owl, cruelly swooping, harass the doomed and desperate swarms. And, last of all, come the familiar followers of routed armies, whether of rats or men: the crows, plundering the wounded and eating the carrion.

If any survivors are left to reach the sea, there are the gulls, petrels and skuas, and as is their way, they let nothing pass; and the almost unanimous opinion of observers is that there is no return migration. Only Hoegstroem, quoted by Brehm, claims to have counted about a hundred survivors making their way in the opposite direction. But in comparison with the total strength of the exodus, these hundred virtually count for nothing.

On a smaller scale, and giving less impression of being subjected to an unchangeable fate, other species, notably the voles, also proliferate excessively in certain years, although the reasons for this have not been clearly established. We will do no more than touch upon them, and will add a few words, before leaving the rodents, on a migratory creature that "colonizes" in the same way as certain insects (Phylloxera, Doryphores) mentioned earlier.

## A World Danger

"It is only nine or ten years since this species spread to the outskirts of Paris. No one knows whence these animals came, but they have multiplied prodigiously. The places where they first appeared, and where their ravages were remarked early on, are Chantilly, Marly-la-Ville and Versailles. M. Leroy, the park inspector, has been good enough to send us a great number, both living and dead, and he has also given us some observations that he has made on this new species."

Who wrote that, and what was it all about?

The author of those lines is Buffon. And the new animal, which he suggested calling the "surmulot," is currently known to us as the sewer rat, or the gray rat, that rat which today teems throughout the whole world, even reaching the most remote desert islands, and which, until 1753, had appeared in Paris only as a rare and curious specimen!

How did it get there, and where did it come from?

It is believed that for thousands of centuries, ever since its emergence as a separate species, it was confined to the Far East, to China. Everywhere else it was unknown.

What took place to bring about the species' worldwide expansion in not much more than two hundred years? Only peevishness, the "breed's ruling spirit," it might be said! Anyway, it was in 1727, according to the naturalist Simon Pallas, that some legions of these rats suddenly appeared on the Volga's eastern bank, where they lingered for a while before finally deciding to cross the river, drowning in it by the million. Then, not noticeably diminished, they invaded the Ukraine, crossing the Dnieper, the Bug and the Dniester, always driving further and further westward, presently overrunning Galicia, and Bohemia a little later. By 1740 they were already giving trouble in East Prussia, where, until then unknown, they astonished the populace by suddenly appearing in huge numbers; and thirteen years later there were a few in Paris. Today, there are millions. During the first half of the nineteenth century the entire planet became their habitat, and with them, they brought their fleas. And their fleas brought the plague, which kills men as well as rats.

We cannot leave the rodents, which could provide us

with a number of other examples, without at least mentioning the black rat (Linnaeus' *Rattus rattus*), another recent invader of our country, but which certainly seems to have been introduced by man—by the Crusaders' ships, it is said. It is certain that the species was unknown in Western Europe before the Middle Ages, at which time it multiplied rapidly until the arrival of the sewer rat, which, stronger and more belligerent, was not slow to take its place, especially in towns.

Finally, the squirrels deserve mention, if only because they, too, have had the honor of inspiring Chateaubriand, who depicts them for us in sonorous and fulgent words, worthy of recording the voyage of the Argonauts: "The hardy breed, fickle as the waves, yet fiercely possessed by their inconstancy, at once spread their tails like sails of silk to the wind, carried along, reckless pirates, by their love of plunder. . . ." The squirrels also deserve mention because, in present-day France, they appear to effect curious changes of habitat, settling for several years in regions where they have never been seen in living memory. E. Maistre comments upon, and examines, "the appearance of squirrels in the Bas-Languedoc and the Montagne Noire around 1917," giving us many interesting details regarding this immigration. A. Hughes, with his usual competence, describes similar occurrences in the moorlands of the Gard.

## Where Do the Bats Go?

Only in recent times have naturalists drawn attention to the migration of the chiropters. Buffon simply notes that all bats "spend the winter without moving and without eating, only waking up in the spring, then going into hiding anew toward the end of autumn." He makes no allusion to their journeys, and his successors seem to have been equally ignorant of them. However, about 1800, J. M. Bechstein, the German naturalist, put forward the hypothesis that bats undertake annual journeys, but he was given little attention. In 1857 Blasius established that *Vesperuga borealis* is observable in transition periodically in northern Germany; and in 1870 Trouessart observed the migrations of the kalong and others among the large tropical fructivorous species, then later, among some of the bats of our latitudes. But it was not until 1890 that Otto Hepp witnessed, on an autumn day, bats mingled with swallows passing over the Main River in considerable numbers at an altitude of some two hundred feet, and flying in an east-to-west direction.

Since then observations have proliferated, and conducted methodically, they have opened new horizons as regards the biology of these creatures.

Without referring to all the naturalists who have applied themselves to the problem, and mentioning simply our compatriots, A. Hughes and E.-L. Trouessart, we will summarize the most recent researches that have notably advanced the study.

It is through the technique of ringing that these results have been obtained. Ringing consists in fastening a light aluminum band to some part of the animal. This ring bears various particulars that will show, if a specimen is recaptured, where and when it was released.

With birds, the operation is easy, and the ring is placed on the leg. But before bats could be dealt with suitably, some trial-and-error was necessary. Today, a tiny clasp clipped to the wing at the level of the arm gives complete satisfaction.

This technique, inaugurated in Germany and America with considerable success, has been adopted in France by N. Casteret under the influence of Bourdelle and the Station française de Baguage du Muséum, and for several years Casteret has carried out interesting observations on bats of various species frequenting the Tignahustes cave in the Hautes-Pyrénées, as well as on a great number of individual specimens (cf. *Mammalia,* March, 1938 and March, 1939).

The cave is chiefly inhabited in summer by Miniopterae, and especially Murinae (*Myotis myotis*), one of the largest species found in France, which has some two dozen varieties. At other times, some horseshoe bats and naked-faced bats are found there, but these are soon expelled by the newcomers, which are much stronger and more combative. Murinae remains the final occupant, since, after mixing with Miniopterae for a while, it evicts it as soon as the members of the latter give birth.

Ordinarily the bats appear in the second half of March, simultaneously with the first swallows. They come in small groups, and within the space of a few days several hundred individual bats occupy the cave. One strange detail: if then, or at any time during their stay in the cave, bats are captured, it is found that in Miniopterae the numbers of males and females are clearly equal, but the Murinae are exclusively female, yet all are fertilized, since early in June all have offspring, usually one, more rarely two. Where are the males at this time? As yet, no one knows.

Throughout the summer the bats leave the cave to forage immediately after sunset, and virtually all return five or six hours later.

Departure takes place in the second half of August. "This stay of four and a half months coincides with the period of gestation, parturition and lactation. As soon as they are weaned and able to fly, the 470 young murines leave with their 400 mothers. It has not been possible to study the Minopterae with the same degree of precision."

As yet it is not possible to say where these bats go in the winter. Since they are seen mixed in with flocks of swallows and martins, it is not improbable that they accompany them—to Africa, perhaps—and experiments on them heretofore have mainly concerned their migratory orientation. Some of several murines, released in different directions, were recaptured after traveling only 125 miles. Nevertheless it should be kept in mind that some bats released from a balcony on the outskirts of Paris—that is, some four hundred miles from the Tignahustes caves—set off southward without hesitation.

Moreover, Casteret draws attention to this suggestive detail concerning some captive bats that were being transported by rail: "The bats, which were quiet and calm throughout the long journey, became extremely agitated and noisy between the Montréjeau and Lannemezan stations, where the train passes quite close to the Tignahustes caves."

Let us end by quoting the present record for a murine, held by one that, ringed at Dresden, was recaptured in Lithuania, a distance of nearly five hundred miles.

## *Marine Migrants*

Following the flying mammals, some words must be said about those mammals that are exclusively swimmers, and with them we will end this rapid over-all survey of the migratory behavior of this class of vertebrates.

The insectivores need not detain us, and as for monkeys, they can on the whole be thought of as nomads rather than true migrants. Nevertheless the howling monkeys, inhabiting the forests of Central America, must be briefly mentioned, since in certain circumstances, and probably under the influence of food-shortages due to overpopulation, they abandon *en masse* the territory in which they have lived until then, and suddenly appear, numerous and in packed ranks, in regions where they have never been seen.

The pinnipeds comprise the seals, sea lions and walruses, and with them we find ourselves confronting animals that, in certain respects remind us of the fish we have already studied, and even of birds, from a particular viewpoint and to a greater degree than one would think from their appearance and environment. Like both fish and birds, it is primarily to return to their birthplaces for mating and reproduction that they regularly travel great distances. They do this with a perseverance that nothing can check, and men have known only too well how to profit from this.

As a representative example, we will select the fur seal or sea bear (Linnaeus' *Otaria ursina*), whose characteristic habits have long been studied by the fur-trappers.

These animals were once distributed over the whole of

the North Pacific, from California to Japan and eastern Siberia. Today their number is greatly diminished, and they have only avoided total annihilation by a small margin, thanks to laws too long delayed. Certain of the Pribilof Islands (lat. 57° N. long. 170° E.) in the Bering Sea between Alaska and Kamchatka, form one of their last refuges. And this is where we will visit them, under the guidance of H. W. Elliot, the naturalist who studied them most closely.

The first males, coming from the south, reach the islands at the beginning of May. Others are not slow to follow, and then bloody battles break out to secure the best places, on the land nearest to the beaches. By the time the females arrive in the course of June, order has been established to such purpose that the most vigorous males are the first to receive them, and have first choice of them. However, these foremost seals, kept busy by driving off their rivals, are rarely able to reserve more than three or four dozen females for themselves, and the seals consigned to the secondary area—that is, those thrust down to about the twentieth place in the order of things—come into their own and take over the released outnumbered females, forcing them to follow by biting them, or by dragging them along by the scruffs of their necks. And thus they become the lords and masters of a dozen or so slaves. The seals of the third area have to content themselves by grabbing four or five seals from those left over, while the crippled and the defeated, thrust furthest into the island's interior, are reduced to celibacy. Nevertheless they could fare worse, since the lucky sultans of the forward areas, waxing fat and strong in their chosen paradise, soon exhaust themselves by waging endless battles, not even sparing the time to eat, in defense of their females.

In the autumn, all the surviving seals vanish, returning to the warmer waters of the south, where they spend the winter.

A large number of pinnipeds have comparable habits, while others are sedentary. As regards these animals, it is clear that their movements are principally conditioned by the question of food supplies, and that their migrations follow those of the fish that form their staple. The question of temperature also plays a part.

Finally, to end this survey of migratory mammals, we will content ourselves with a brief mention of the cetaceans, most of which certainly undertake long and periodic journeys, but as yet not enough is known of these to determine their routes and extent. However, it is known that the white whales, which give birth off the California coast, spend the summer in the Arctic Ocean, and that the humpback whales, inhabiting tropical waters in the winter, return to the Antarctic in summer.

## 4 / The Migrations of Birds

Now we enter the realm of the supreme migratory creatures, the characteristic displacements of which have been noticed in all ages by even the least observant, and which, thanks to the exceptional superiority of their means of locomotion, can travel immense distances without being deflected from their goal by material obstacles.

We have mentioned the swallow as being the traditional symbol of this type of migrant. But we shall see that in fact the choice could as well have fallen on any one of a hundred others; and besides, it cannot be limited exclusively to any one *species*. Nevertheless, as a matter of convenience, and because the swallow's familiar image can be called to mind by those of us who are no ornithologists, we provisionally intend to take this bird as our model.

For a start, just what is a swallow?

Everyone supposes he can answer such a question with absolute certainty. If, however, to put that certainty to the test, we review the evidence of specialists, we find that the true swallows alone comprise more than forty different species. Or, sixty-five to seventy, if we include martins (although only a portion of these frequent our latitudes).

No doubt some people will complacently add swifts to these, asking if they are not much the same thing. Here, however, some attention must be paid to the naturalists by acknowledging that they are not splitting hairs or chasing the moonbeams of an over-meticulous classification when they place swifts quite apart from swallows. The differences between the two groups are far more important and far less superficial than the resemblances, and a total separation is fully justified.

Having made this clear, we return to our chosen example, conferring this role specifically upon the house swallow (Linnaeus' *Hirundo rustica*), which everyone knows and will recognize from the following brief description: short beak, long wings, forked tail, blue-black head and back, reddish-brown throat and breast, white belly with russet tints, a builder of nests under eaves and cornices and beneath the roof beams of barns and stables; and so on.

Now let us study this bird's migratory behavior.

### *"A swallow, on its way . . ."*

In central France the first isolated house swallows reappear during the first half of April. For centuries observers have noticed that the same pair returns to its former nest, sometimes for several years in succession; and this constancy, together with the bird's familiarity, its gracefulness, the obvious services it renders us by destroying innumerable noxious insects, and its annual return, which coincides with that of spring, all tend to create an indulgent attitude, even in men who otherwise have little respect for animal life. However, this does not prevent its being caught for food in some countries, although it is almost inedible.

When the nest does not already exist, the swallow builds it by collecting tiny fragments of soil and sticking them with its saliva to an "armature" of straw and various other weather-resistant materials.

The female fixes the nest, shaped like a half-basin, to a vertical support, such as a buttress, the angle between two walls, the corner of a window or chimney, and so on. The nest's walls are thick, and its interior is lined with feathers, moss and shreds of wool. This padding is renewed every year, even if the previous year's is still serviceable.

In May the female lays some eggs, which she alone sits on, and which take a fortnight to hatch out. The young birds grow rapidly, and by the end of June are already able to try out their wings. There is nearly always a second brood toward midsummer and, much more rarely, a third.

With the coming of autumn the swallows start to show the first signs of their approaching departure.

Although so far the pairs, or at most, the families, have lived independently of the other swallows, now the birds are seen to congregate in increasingly greater numbers in any places where they can perch side by side—on rooftops, telegraph wires, bushes and reeds—together with birds of other species. Each swallow seems to press against its neighbor, carrying on with it an animated conversation, interrupted from time to time by a brief moment of flight and a quick return. And as autumn advances, these meetings become more and more frequent and regular.

Then, at sunset on an evening in October, the whole flock rises as one into the air in answer to a signal that certainly appears to be given by means of a birdcall having the effect of an order. They soar higher, wheeling a few times, then, still soaring, disappear from view. The swallows have gone, not to return for six months.

The regularity of these singular movements, and their periodicity, related so exactly to that of the seasons, have in all ages attracted man's attention. And yet the explanation— that of an annual journey to climates less severe than our own—has been known only a short time. From antiquity to our own time, but especially in the Middle Ages and throughout the Renaissance, there have been authors, and not the least of them, who have maintained that swallows spend the winter asleep in the mud on the bottoms of ponds, sometimes even being caught by anglers in compact and somnolent clusters.

It is pointless to say that this is no more than a legend. But if we assume that this is not mere superstition, and ask ourselves how such a crude idea, with no factual basis, could have come about, we pick up some sketchy clues quite easily. Undoubtedly some swallows, unable to depart with the others, do occasionally spend the winter in our country, apparently becoming torpid—like bats and various other hibernating animals—and only awakening during the warmest hours of mild days to find a little food. Most of us have seen, if only once, one of these lonely birds fly past and vanish silently on an afternoon in November or January, leaving us filled with mingled surprise and doubt. Where did it come from? Where has it been hiding? The question is still very puzzling and much debated.

Be that as it may, the immense majority of swallows do migrate. Where do they go?

At various times attempts have been made to discover this by giving one of the migrants a distinctive mark; and a little later we shall see to what degree this technique, applied on a large scale and methodically controlled, has encouraged important progress in the recent study of migration. Indeed, the idea was thought of in classical times, but a few isolated and maladroit attempts to use it produced only some unsatisfactory results.

Buffon remarked shrewdly: "Aristotle, writing in Athens, and Pliny, copying him in Rome, said that swallows went away to spend the winter in climates with a milder temperature. . . ." But at the same time he noted that these authors referred only to short migrations to neighboring countries. Studying the question in the light of his potent genius, he concluded from the testimony of several travelers "that great multitudes of house swallows arrive in Senegal about the ninth of October and depart from there in the spring. . . ." And on the basis of these facts, he decided that "these birds, when they can no longer find the insects that suit them in a particular country, fly toward less cold regions that offer them an abundance of this prey, lacking which they cannot survive." And, with his intuitive gift for supplying answers to questions that could not then be resolved by the evidence of experiments he added:

I maintain that this first cause is supported by another that also influences bird migration, or at least induces the birds to return to the country in which they were born. A bird may change its climate, but it has a fatherland, and like any other creature, it recognizes, and is attached to, the haunts in which it first saw the light, where it first exercised its faculties, first experienced sensations and had its first inklings of what life might hold. It only leaves such places with regret, and when it is forced to by dearth. An irresistible yearning constantly calls it back, and this yearning, combined with its knowledge of a route already traveled, and with the strength of its wings, puts it in the position of being able to return to its native land whenever there is the hope of finding amenities and subsistence there.

If the solution of this complicated problem is not entirely provided by this brief passage, at least two of its most important and incontestable elements are indicated: the search for food and the return to the nest. Certainly these are the two chief causes of migration; but they are far from being the only ones, as we shall soon see.

Indeed, when we approach the question a little closer, we find it by no means simple. An example taken from those over which we have most control will convince us of this.

We said above that, morphologically speaking, the swifts are quite different from the swallows. Yet, considering them within the limits of our subject, they resemble them in their choice of food and their way of securing it, in their habitats, and in the punctuality of their departures and returns. Purely insectivorous, like the swallows, they ought, when the time comes, to obey the same migratory demands.

Yet we know that they do nothing of the sort. The swifts arrive in our region a month later than the swallows, and they leave again about the end of August. In other words, they arrive long after their food supplies have become largely assured, and they leave when these supplies are at their most plentiful—with the weather at its warmest, with nothing to warn them that a change of climate is imminent, or that that climate's food resources will presently diminish.

In passing, let us note the relationship established by birds between the periods of time that separate the dates of their arrival and departure from the solstice.

A migrant such as the starling, which arrives in January or February, generally does not go until November or December, whereas a laggard, such as the golden oriole, nicknamed "the Pentecost bird" because it appears at about Whitsun, leaves again in August, and is sometimes so anxious to get away that it imperils the fate of its young.

## Sedentary Birds and Accidental Migrants

We cannot select certain outstanding examples to illustrate bird migration, as we did with other classes of animals, since such a selection would invite a one-sided attitude, and nothing justifies a preference detrimental to a host of identical cases. We must adopt another form of presentation.

Indeed, almost all birds are migratory, or at least nomadic; that is, even if they do not undertake distant journeys at fixed periods and short intervals, they at least constantly change localities in the course of the year, here today and gone tomorrow, with hardly a pause except in the nesting season. Truly sedentary birds are a minority, and the classic type is the gray partridge, which stays in the same neighborhood where it was originally hatched all year round. This species has spread throughout Europe, but it is much more localized in some forms, for instance, the famous grouse (*Lagopus scoticus*), which in England is found south to the 54th parallel and north to the Orkneys.

Moreover, certain sedentary species are only partially so. One example, and there are others, is the rook, which has been closely studied in France during the last few years by the ornithological station at Versailles. It has been established that some rooks remain in the vicinity of their native rookeries, while others regularly pass through the Belfort Gap on their return from their Central European migrations, then leave France via the Pyrenees.

Although we lack sufficient space to dwell on such groups, mention must be made of those species that, as regards France, are classed as "accidentals"—birds that appear only at intervals, sometimes very long ones. These capricious habits do not help to elucidate a problem already quite obscure enough without them.

A notable example is Pallas' sand grouse (*Syrrhaptes paradoxus* Pallas), a strange bird that is certainly paradoxical enough to justify its specific epithet. More or less intermediary between the gallinaceous birds and the pigeons, it normally inhabits the desert steppes of Central Asia, where it lives in large flocks that travel in serried flights.

At certain intervals—which can exceed a human generation, and which so far we are unable to predict—the syrrhaptes leave their native land in huge flocks, sometimes going as far toward the west as is possible for them, since some alight in England or even in Ireland, living for a time where they land, making some attempts at reproduction, and leaving behind those infrequent pairs that manage to rear some young as if they intended to install themselves indefinitely. However, these attempts are doomed to failure. Soon the last of the visitors has gone, and long years pass before they are seen again.

The first of these invasions officially recorded took place in 1839; others followed in 1872, 1888 and 1913, that of 1888 being by far the most important. And today we are no better informed about the true causes of these unforeseen migrations than we were a hundred years ago!

Other birds, such as the Bohemian waxwing, the crossbill, the Siberian jay, and so on, pose similar riddles, which we are just as unable to answer.

Of course, there are many other sedentary birds than the ones we know, and if, in spite of everything, food and temperature do remain important in determining migration, we ought to find some species in increasingly greater numbers as we approach the warmer countries.

Indeed, this is what often happens, although not invariably. For one thing, all those birds that leave our latitudes in the winter spend that season in the tropics; but they do not stay there indefinitely, which is on the whole difficult to explain, since conditions are as good for them there when they depart as when they arrive. And for another thing, some species very closely related to those we know to be the most inveterate migrants, sometimes identical with them, stay on in the warm regions when the others depart. There are some swallows, swifts and water birds, and so on, that never leave Central Africa or Equatorial Asia. But who knows why? Moreover—quite apart from those species that cannot fly—there are some that stay in very confined areas; and islands, as we know, often have a large number of birds not found elsewhere. The avifauna of Madagascar and New Guinea, among others, is extremely specific to those islands—this used to be even more so— while on St. Helena there is a small plover never met with anywhere else, although the breed as a whole heads the list of long-distance migrants.

Yet neither isolation imposed by the sea, nor a lesser or greater degree of inaptitude for flight, are the only reasons for these sedentary habits. Some birds, such as the curious baloeniceps, to give one example, can accomplish long journeys when the fancy takes them. Yet the baloeniceps hardly ever leaves the region of the Upper Nile, where it must meet a host of winter visitors, some of them close relatives. But these appear quite unable to persuade it to "see the world" with them.

### Irregular Migrants

In this group we shall put those varieties alluded to earlier as only making small journeys at short intervals. These consequently did not at once catch the attention of the naturalists, who took them for sedentary birds, without realizing that it was not the same individual bird they were seeing throughout the year.

Here there are many more examples than in the category just dealt with, and for a start we can include the majority of "those little birds" of La Fontaine's fable mentioned in our opening chapter, with this reservation—that "at the time of hemp-sowing" most of them have already departed or have not arrived, any more than has the swallow who advises them. But this is only a detail.

It seems quite natural for the insectivorous passerines not to spend the winter in our climate, where their normal routine would break down. Many tits, warblers and so on are in this class, but with the nightingale, they can be compared to regular migrants, and concerning them we shall have more to say. In fact, every degree of migration is discernible in their habits.

Some, such as nightingales, cuckoos and so on, arrive and depart on precise dates as regularly as the swallows. Others, the majority, are more capricious, making their way by short stages, quite independent of the calendar, delaying where they find they must, then going like the wind when no one can say what makes them hurry, and often retracing their steps for reasons we cannot encompass—although this, of course, does not discourage the theorists.

Meanwhile other birds of the same species stay with us all the time, even though the main part of their food supply has gone, and we cannot see what prevents their following it in this case more than any other.

Such is the case with the robins, among others. During the summer these familiar little inhabitants of our gardens make ruthless war on the worms, snails and insects and their larvae, and most of them depart when they find themselves deprived of their food supplies. Nevertheless an important number stay with us throughout the winter, harassed by feeding problems to the point of begging part of their subsistence from man, and getting from him only an unsuitable diet. For all that, the robin persists in staying on, in spite of the cold (to which the species is sensitive), in spite of the food shortage (particularly hard for creatures endowed with an insatiable appetite), in spite of all the instincts that influence others of the breed, and that ought also to prevail over these obstinate individuals. In fact, if certain theories are to be believed, it is impossible for them to resist!

A fair number of sea birds must also be included among the irregular migrants.

Most of the gulls that we see at the seaside during the season and that—at least during fine weather—seem as happy to be there as ourselves, are in reality migrants constantly replacing one another. Except during the nesting season, this species can be considered to be in a state of perpetual migration from one end of the year to the other.

In winter they take off from some southerly point and make their way by short stages toward the north, progressing slowly along beaches, sometimes forced inland by gales or cold, scratching for food in plowed fields or among crops, foraging along the banks of ponds and streams, retracing their steps when it pleases them to do so—or rather, when urged by some unknown instinct—then returning once more to their original route.

By the spring they are already far to the north, journey's end, where they plan to nest. There, where they were themselves hatched out, they know of undisturbed refuges where their eggs can be laid and the young ones reared. As soon as the young gulls have learned to fly—that is, in summer, when there are still long weeks of easy and plentiful living ahead—the return journey nevertheless begins, and is carried out in the same way as the first.

A large number of mountain birds are also irregular migrants—for instance, the tichodrome, or the snow finch— but their migrations are more vertical than horizontal. They spend the summer at high altitudes, then go down to the valleys in winter, seeking a milder climate and sources of food to replace those that will be shrouded beneath snow for many months.

How ought we to classify those cosmopolitan birds that have no specific habitat? Some eminent modern ornithologists, following the lead of Marcel de Serres, the first to suggest it, would make a separate group of them, placing in it species that extend all over the world—such as the common wild duck—and those dispersed over vast areas—such as the albatross. All these they would describe as "cosmopolites," but as J. Oberthur has so rightly pointed out, this epithet could be applied without distinction both to some migratory birds, such as the terns, and to some birds that are strictly sedentary, such as the raven and the barn owl. So, agreeing with the last author, we stress that the term "cosmopolite" cannot be considered a specific classification, and is only valuable as a descriptive label useful, in particular cases, in each of the other divisions.

## Migrants by Degree

In this category we place those birds that migrate regularly every year, but that do not hurry to reach their goal, and instead, stop here and there on the way for shorter or longer periods.

Thus we distinguish these from the irregular migrants more from our viewpoint as observers than from the viewpoint of the birds' habits. That is to say, we are apt to think of the irregular migrants as sedentary, since we go on seeing roughly the same number of birds in the same places, whereas as regards those that carry out their migrations by stages, one day they are plentiful and the next absent, and most often we see them in transit with only a few or none nesting in our neighborhood—their visit generally lasts less than a season, except during the winter cold. Also, we must take into account those species in which no behavior is immutable; and again it must be remembered that what is the rule in, say, the north or the south, may be the exception in the west or the east, and vice versa.

Thus the woodcock, to the benefit of sportsmen, can well be taken as the best example of these temporary visitors met with only in the cold months, while others of the same species know from experience that our climate is suitable for nesting. There are even some among these succulent birds that leave our latitudes at any time of the year —no doubt with the intention of confusing our classifications and obscuring the reason for the migratory habits of the majority!

We could find even better examples by investigating other species, such as the barnacle goose, or the marèque, or even the golden plover, as well as some birds of prey. But let us spend no more time on the representatives of this section, but pass on to the next, which will provide some less wayward types.

## Direct Migrants

These are the "calendar birds" beyond compare, the precision tools of the immense migratory apparatus, otherwise so erratic. These birds, leaving on an almost fixed date, arrive at their objective without loitering on the way. They do not migrate in a single non-stop journey—as is sometimes believed and stated—but at least any stops they are obliged to make, usually owing to weather conditions, are not prolonged beyond the necessity, and are generally very short.

In this category we should expect to find once again our familiar swallow, and indeed its name is among the first on a long list that, in our climate, ought perhaps to be headed by the swift. This little bird is especially remarkable for the precision of its date of arrival, which, in Paris, never strays from the first of May by more than a few days— usually later, but occasionally earlier.

As regards the majority of birds in this group, their forceful way of flying, the power of their motor muscles, and the ease with which they maneuver in the air probably all help to account for the speed of their journeys. For instance, when a rare and happy circumstance offers us the splendid and fascinating spectacle of a flock of cranes flying in wedge formation against the wind, necks outstretched like ships' figureheads, powerful wings slowly beating, we know for sure that they will reach their objective when they intend and as planned; and many other long-distance migrants share their lot and have the same attributes.

Not all. Quails, which appear so clumsy in flight when they rise from beneath a dog's nose, must nevertheless be considered direct migrants, pausing but briefly during daylight to eat and sleep, and by night taking to the air in an impressive departure with more resolution than one would think them capable of. It is hard to explain the need for such efforts, if food and temperature are the only matters involved.

The speed of a bird's flight in itself, then, is not always relevant to the speed of the journey. The legend of the swallows traveling from Africa to France in a night—and they are theoretically capable of it—does not correspond to the facts. These birds, which in full flight can easily reach seventy-five miles an hour, do not cover more than some 250 miles in the twenty-four hours, partly because they forage for food during flight, and partly because they do not fly with all their power, knowing they must keep something in reserve. Some precise observations have enabled us to establish the difference between their average speed in migration, and occasional bursts of acceleration.

On the evidence of a majority of falconers, a peregrine falcon, swooping on its prey, briefly reaches the terrifying speed of 150 miles an hour! During some experiments made in America with a related species, a record speed was obtained of 187 miles an hour—but, of course, only for a few seconds. Yet the same birds in normal flight (timed by the famous ornithological station at Rossitten—clocked less than forty miles an hour, slower than the starling, which normally flies at about forty-six miles an hour, and slower even than the little quail, which, scared by the noise of a shotgun, can persuade its poor rounded wings to make it touch fifty!

To round out this chapter, a distinction must be made, for our latitudes, between summer visitors and winter ones. The first, the most numerous, are all those that come to us from the south in the nesting season from Southern Europe as well as from the tropics, where they have been passing the winter in the warmth.

The others spend the summer, and the larger part of the year, in northern countries, and even in the polar regions, where they nest. However, particularly if the winter is severe, they come to our latitudes in the months that are the coldest for us, but which they appreciate for their temperate mildness compared with what they have left. Swans, and a large number of other web-footed birds, are in this class.

Occasionally, too, during a really exceptional drop in the winter temperature, we are visited by species that are otherwise quite unknown in our latitudes: the whitewing scoter, the ivory gull, the eider duck, the snow goose, the hawk owl and so on.

To complete these examples, we mention a few totally unexpected strays. The captures have been described, in France, of an albatross, a frittillary, a frigate bird and—

acme of surprise—a snake bird, recovered one day from the harbor of Toulon.

## Patterns and Altitudes of Flight

Summing up the preceding examples, it can be seen that migration is not merely a phenomenon that happens at the equinoxes, as is sometimes suggested, but that in reality it takes place throughout the year, with varying intensity, but never showing a total cessation.

Moreover, this intensity is considerably in excess of what is commonly thought. When, at night, the more alert among us chance to hear the sky echo with the muted-oboe call uttered by geese, the flutelike note of curlews, the honking of swans, or the "rusty cries" of cranes, we are apt to suppose this a rare enough occurrence. But if our eyes could pierce the darkness, we could see, at all times, and especially in spring and autumn, birds in passage across the sky unceasingly, so to speak.

Some statistics? Then let us borrow them, as well as a few other details, from C. Aubert's excellent and comprehensive monograph on the migrations of birds,* which, in this connection, quotes Thienemann, who for thirty years was the director of the Rossitten ornithological establishment, where, on occasion, the following flocks of birds were observed in passage:

60,000 crows in two hours; more than 80,000 small birds in two hours; 560,000 birds of various species in two days; 108,000 finches in three hours; and so on. To these

* C. Aubert, *Les migrations des oiseaux* (Paris: Meschers, 1936).

examples, those of migrating pigeons can be added; but they must be counted, not in hundreds of thousands, but in dozens of millions.

If we bear in mind that these figures comprise only the birds the observers have been able to see and count, and that great numbers of others must have gone by in the same period but outside the observer's field of vision, we begin to get some idea of the immensity of these migrations.

Indeed, the examples given deal only with species that fly low, such as crows, which on average hardly rise above 1,200 feet, and at that height appear no larger than dots to the naked eye. Although the majority of species seem to keep at about that altitude, other birds have been observed traveling at far greater ones. Here are some figures selected from data provided either by airborne observers or by astronomical observatories. Starlings, swallows and gulls, seen flying at 3,000 feet; storks, geese and lapwings, at 4,500 feet; ducks, rooks, geese and lapwings, at 4,500 feet to 9,000 feet; finches, at 10,000 feet; buzzards, falcons and thrushes, at 12,000 feet; woodcock, cranes, blackbirds, finches, woodpeckers and plovers, and others, at 15,000 feet. Geese have even been reported at 29,000 feet, but this figure, although quite possible, has not been recorded officially.

We repeat, however, that high altitudes—those above 3,000 to 4,500 feet—*seem to be* the exception rather than the rule. Yet this has not been proved, and opinion is divided. Besides, altitudes vary considerably in relation to atmospheric conditions. Rain, a head wind and so on, tend to drive the migrants toward the ground. In fine weather, with a following wind, and when traveling over sea or, naturally, mountains, they fly much higher.

We have mentioned the different directions of the wind, and also the night. In passing let us bear in mind that neither one factor nor the other prevents migration. Even nighttime seems to favor it—a point we will return to presently.

Note also that in the majority of cases observed—involving some four hundred species—it is generally the young birds that leave first on the outward journey (that is, in our latitudes, the journey toward the south, the warmth), while for the return journey the opposite is true, and it is the fully grown birds that, intending to nest, are the first to leave and arrive. Moreover in both directions it is the males that most often depart alone and ahead. At least this has been observed as regards finches, nightingales, warblers, various ducks and so on; but as regards the garrot ducks, the opposite has been established. In any case, the sexes are frequently separated. One result of this is that quite a number of young males that have not found mates do not pursue the journey to its end—that is, to the species' breeding places—but stop off en route in some pleasant and hospitable region where they wait, in placid celibacy, until the family returns on its way back at the end of the season.

## Extent of Migrations

Finally, to complete these facts before attempting to explain them, we shall say a few words on the extent of the distances traveled.

To measure these distances, it is necessary to "accompany" the birds that traverse them. This is achieved by means of ringing: fixing to the bird's leg a metal ring bearing various marks that will be returned to the sender by whoever recaptures the bird in due course. By this means statistics are collected, which, after collation and averaging, furnish useful and precise information. Today stations where ringing is carried out function in all civilized countries, and annually some hundreds of thousands of birds are marked.

In this way we have learned that although some species do not journey beyond the frontiers of a province, or, even less, merely fly from the mountain heights to the valleys, others travel each year some tens of thousands of miles from their native haunts and faithfully return to them.

This is so, for instance, with storks and swallows, which go to the Cape and to the Indies, some six or seven thousand miles from their nest; and this is not their maximum. Certain plovers travel the whole length of the Americas, from the land of the Eskimos in northern Canada to that of the Fuegians on the southern tip of South America, a total of some nine thousand miles. And we can state as a general rule that "the birds nesting furthest north are those that winter furthest south" (Trouessart).

Again, the great migrations are carried out by stages; but some journeys, in spite of being a little shorter, call for a far greater effort. First place in this category seems to belong to an American golden plover that, taking off from Hawaii regularly every year, spends the mating season in Alaska. This involves a flight of 2,500 miles over the Pacific

Ocean, with nowhere to perch on the way for even a moment's rest.

It remains to say something about the routes followed by migratory birds.

Although this question has been greatly elucidated in recent years—thanks to information obtained by ringing—it cannot yet be condensed into systematic formulae. We shall limit ourselves to outlining the essentials.

One thing is undoubtedly true: if it is certain that the fatherland of an animal is the place where it breeds, the fatherland of the great majority of birds is somewhere in the Northern Hemisphere, since almost all migrations are from this part of the globe toward the equator or beyond, while movements made in the opposite direction are far less important. It is true that there are almost no land areas in the temperate zone of the Southern Hemisphere, but even so, it seems that the Antarctic's few species are far less migratory than those of the Arctic. In contrast, many species of our latitudes—swallows, quails, storks, ducks, plovers and so on—go for the winter to the furthest ends of Asia and tropical Africa.

As for the route taken, in general they are always the same for the same species. They are numerous. Some idea can be given of them, as regards our part of the world, by thinking of an open fan having its bottom part in the tropics in West Africa, while its top part spreads over Northern Europe and Asia from Siberia to Iceland.

In the Western Hemisphere, where the continents are longitudinally narrower, these migratory movements can be observed more precisely, and consequently, it has been found that the outward route is not always the same as the return route. Indeed, it has been established that the itinerary of certain plovers runs from Alaska across Canada to Newfoundland, then passes over the sea for 2,500 miles, which takes it as far as Guiana, whence the birds continue south until they reach Patagonia; but the return journey takes them straight up the west coast of the continent until they arrive back at their starting point.

In conclusion, we should point out that even in the tropics sedentary birds are the exception, and huge migrations have been observed moving from one side of the equator to the other.

Now we have enough examples and plenty of material. Let us see if we can make something of them.

# 5 / Conclusions

In scientific matters, even when there is general agreement concerning the facts, there is often far less when it comes to explaining them.

Does this then mean that no one can explain them satisfactorily? Among so many theories, some corroborating each other, some in conflict, is there not one that governs the others, one that can induce unanimity of opinion? Does the best of them show some defect, leave some lacuna unfilled, totter on its foundations? In a word, it is false?

If so, there would be more to rejoice about than to lament over, since this would once more open up an immense field for research, one to delight the human mind by its wealth of fertile possibilities. The trouble is that many of those who venture into the field are so understandably pleased with their gleanings that they have only disdain for what others have found, and the impartial inquirer who follows in their footsteps finds himself much hampered when he has to make a sheaf from all that has been garnered. Which, from so many arbitrary and exclusive theories, is he to select and adopt?

If he wants to put prudence before the satisfaction of having an opinion of his own, there are some themes that he must hurl from him at the very outset, so as to be sure of never touching upon them and thus bringing unanimous execration upon himself. On the subject that occupies us here, the two most deplorable tendencies anyone can let himself be tempted by are, in the eyes of modern science, anthropomorphism and teleology. To attempt to understand the behavior of animals, even the higher ones, by asking what we, mankind would do in the same circumstances, is utterly useless. To want to see in animal behavior an effort, even a blind one, toward a purposeful goal for the creature that makes it, is childishness. Let us hide our heads and look further!

These easy conclusions have quite certainly been abused. When the scientist Louis Agassiz, quoted by Romanes, tells us, speaking of snails, that "whoever has had occasion to observe them making love will know better than to doubt the seductiveness revealed by the behavior and movements that lead up to, and bring about, the double embraces of these hermaphrodites," he certainly exaggerates; and when the good Bernardin de Saint-Pierre tells us that "nature has tipped the ermine's tail with black so that these little white animals, when moving over the snow, can see where to go by following each other," he doubtless credits nature with inspirations that are entirely his own. On the other hand, the fact that we are totally unable to say why

the ermine has a black tail—an invariable characteristic of
the whole species—should not make us conclude that there
is no reason whatsoever for it. And if the snail's coy love-
making is not quite in the same class as that of Circe or
Melusina, we can at the same time reject the comparison as
being a little oversimplified and repeat, with Georges
Leroy, that admirable firsthand observer of wild animals:
"I have lived for a long time with animals, I have studied
many species with a great deal of attention, and I have
learned that the moral and ethical values of wolves can
throw light upon those of men."

Yet, to return to our original question, if we refuse
to regard our migrants as Agassiz regarded his mollusc, how
do we go about explaining them?

Tropisms have been suggested. We have recorded this
hypothesis in passing in connection with fish and insects. Let
us return to it.

This theory, thought out by Loeb at the end of the last
century, and upheld by his disciples, is an extremely con-
venient one, and has a simplicity that makes it clearly at-
tractive.

However, if for want of a better it is acceptable when
applied to inferior organisms, whose behavior cannot in any
way be interpreted by comparing it with our own, it soon
becomes debatable when applied, by itself, to a slightly
higher animal. For such an animal seems to be governed—
as Manquat puts it in a closely argued thesis—by the "law
of its own interests" and by a "biological determinism," i.e.,
by an influence that is *within it,* and not exclusively outside

it, in the way that the wind is outside the reed it bends, while the reed can do nothing to stop it.

When we examine the matter more closely, we see that tropisms help to confirm certain facts, but that they scarcely explain them, since to say that an animal reacts positively or negatively to light, warmth, oxygen, salt, and so on, is not far from saying that opium has soporific properties. The observed fact is certainly true. The adult salmon is certainly attracted to, and drawn toward, water with a high oxygen content; but what sort of mechanism releases this proclivity? Does giving it a Greek name tell us any more about it? And the "blind instinct" dear to some authors is hardly as informative, and certainly not more.

For there was, and still is, the theory of infallible instinct. This, discovered by science relatively recently, is a descendant of Descartes' "animal spirits." In our own time, one of its most confirmed champions was J. H. Fabre. "Instinct," Fabre says, "knows everything in the immutable channels it has developed, and it ignores everything outside those channels. Sublimely scientific inspirations, and astonishingly inconsequent stupidities, are equally its heritage, according to whether the animal is acting in normal conditions or fortuitous ones."

In other words, instinct is an immutable property of living matter, transmitted to creatures by a supernatural power to insure their conservation, irrespective of their own efforts. These creatures have no consciousness of it, and cannot modify it in any way. It alone knows its ends, and always makes directly for them.

The transformists, and many others, have attacked this

theory, demolishing it with no great difficulty: it had foundations of a clay rather too soft to withstand them. It was a dogma that had to be accepted without discussion, and to ask this was to ask an obedience too blind for the spirit of scientific inquiry to accept for long.

Yet once the citadel had been overthrown, was there no further use to which its stones could have been put? And has anyone replaced it by an edifice of such new and imperishable materials that the old ruins can be thrown to the winds like a heap of ashes?

The fact is that Darwin's observation regarding this suspect word "instinct" can still be accepted without offense to any one, subject to such modifications as it admits of:

> I will not attempt any definition of instinct. It would be easy to show that several distinct mental actions are commonly embraced by this term; but everyone understands what is meant, when it is said that instinct impels the cuckoo to migrate and to lay her eggs in other birds' nests. An action, which we ourselves require experience to enable us to perform, when performed by an animal, more especially by a very young one, without experience, and when performed by many individuals in the same way, without their knowing for what purpose it is performed, is usually said to be instinctive.

With these reservations established, it is easier for us to speak of the *instinct* of migration in animals, and to demonstrate the various theories that have attempted to explain it.

Quite probably the disputes and misunderstandings attaching to this subject derive from the phenomenon being considered in its entirety as applying to the whole animal kingdom, and from attributing to all animals, no matter which, the same reactions to the same stimuli, irrespective of the essential differences dividing them.

Naturally, there are certain laws that apply to everything that lives, and each creature has to obey them irrespective of its place in the order of things. Although earlier we refused to "humanize" the snail to the degree asked of us, we can nevertheless return to the idea and, at times, find it valid. In the final analysis, when Armide casts her love spells upon Renaud in the enchanted gardens, the secretions of her ductless glands have something in common with those of the snail, but this, we venture to suggest, is the only point of similarity between the sorceress and the gastropod, and Armide brings to the game many more evidences of her passion, and these of a complexity undreamed of by snails. In fact, it is far more difficult to compare the two than to contrast them.

Much the same is true for our migrants. We shall see that apparently there is, in the recurring desire to migrate, a common stimulus correctly recognizable as similar to the chemical effect that tormented both Armide and the snail. We have already alluded to it as regards insects, fish and mammals, and we shall extend the allusion to birds. However, ignoring the fact that the sedentary creatures are also exposed to the same external stimulus as the migrants without its constituting for them "an invitation to the journey," it is difficult to compare at every point a large vertebrate's behavior with that of a crustacean or a worm, and it seems more sensible to examine each separately.

As regards the inferior forms, from insects to fish, we have discussed the hypotheses suggested by their habits as far as possible in our necessarily condensed chapters, and we shall not return to them. Instead, we leave the obscure still obscure, since no one has as yet provided the means of throwing light on the problems, and we cannot hope to succeed where the most knowledgeable have failed.

As for the mammals, the search for food certainly appears to dominate all other causes of their migratory movements, and the retreat from the cold is no more than its corollary. We have seen that these influences are not always irresistible, that some individuals and some groups escape them, or refuse to submit to them, without our knowing at all clearly why; and we have also seen that instinct can sometimes be guilty of flagrant error.

Yet here again we must not exaggerate.

The implacable enemies of the theory of instinct reject it with such force that they are even reluctant to admit certain proved facts tending to support it, facts that the theory's enemies do not even try to explain in any other way.

The question of the return to the breeding grounds is an example. Some authors deny, as a foregone conclusion, the ability—admittedly sometimes quite astonishing—of animals to follow a route that they have never followed before, or to know what direction to take if there is no factor of associative memory to remind them of it.

Without wasting our time on a debate in which all those who have spent their lives observing free animals at first-hand—hunters, gamekeepers, trappers and so on—

would seem to have quite as much right to a hearing as the theorists and scientists, let us simply recall the Tigna-hustes bats, which displayed a marked agitation when passing the point nearest to their breeding place.

We have neither reason nor right to assume an error of interpretation on the part of an experienced and knowledgeable observer such as Norbert Casteret. We have still to find the explanation of a fact of this sort, and we recognize that this is not easy. If the reactions of a special organ peculiar to these animals do not provide the explanation, as is more than probable, it would at least appear that they have a hypersensitivity in certain of their senses—hearing, perhaps, or smell—such as we can have no idea of.

However, it is the migration of birds that is most susceptible to theories and discussion, and it is time to survey them.

## In Search of Eternal Spring

One widely accepted theory on the cause of migrations is based on paleontology and our planet's history.

We know that in the course of the distant past the earth underwent quite different climatic conditions from those of the present time. On the evidence of considerations it would take too long to explore here, the geologists agree that between the end of the Secondary division and the beginning of the Tertiary—a matter of some three or four hundred million years, according to the most cautious estimates—the globe's climate, although starting to cool down and to show seasonal variations, was much warmer than today. Boule tells us that during the Eocene period "the arctic regions had a climate approximating to that of the present-day temperate zone, and the latter had a subtropical climate . . . France's average temperature, which is now 11° C., would then have been 25° C."

The birds, timidly appearing from the middle of the Secondary division on, and still in a state of flux as regards their destiny (they were still closely related to the reptiles), suddenly took a huge upward flight at the start of the Tertiary division, and acquired forms very close to some present-day species, if not identical with them, as is proved by countless fossil remains found in our time. Many of these fossils, plentiful in France, correspond to types of bird now encountered only in warm countries, and, more particularly in tropical Africa. At a later period, the same considerations were to apply as regards mammals, which, even when man first appeared on the scene, still included elephants, hippopotamuses, apes and lions, in our latitudes.

It is logical to suppose that at that time the animals were not migratory. Why should they have been? Food supplies were abundant and assured from one year to the next. Whether the birds were insectivorous or granivorous, their chosen foods were available all the time, and if the temperature showed some variation, it never dropped low enough to be unendurable.

However, diverse and complicated causes gradually influenced the seasons to vary to an increasingly greater extent, and the climate as a whole grew cooler. Some mammals, more resistant or slower to move, were protected by thick fur, and adapted themselves. Others moved further and further toward the low latitudes, whether temporarily or permanently. As for birds, the ease with which they could move from place to place enabled them to follow the sun, until, erratically and by degrees, they learned how to spend the whole year in a warm climate. Nevertheless, faithful to the place of their birth (which certainly seems to be a biological law), they returned to it every spring, and from generation to generation. In this way the migratory movement established itself and became a law.

Such is one of the chief theories purporting to explain the origins and cause of migration.

Before we examine the criticisms that have been leveled at it, let us touch upon a thesis directly opposed to it, one that also has its supporters. (The reader should not be too surprised by these contradictory opinions: they are the general rule. And, as we pointed out, they show us that the field is still wide open for research.)

According to this other theory, birds originated in those regions that are still the warmest, and have always been so. As long as their numbers were small, life would be easy for them, and each bird would find more than enough food at hand to eliminate any need to migrate.

However, in these favorable conditions, and with no dangerous enemies, their numbers would naturally increase to such a degree that the least combative among them would be forced to find somewhere else to live. Then they would gradually spread toward the higher latitudes in order to nest in peace, but once this important duty was fulfilled, would return to the warmer regions; while the young birds, subject to the law that enforces a return to the breeding place, would obey it in each succeeding year, and their nests would be dispersed in the area around their native nest, now occupied once again by the parent birds.

At first glance, we might think that this hypothesis was conceived solely for the sake of contradicting the other theory. However, it is supported by demonstrable facts, and notably by observation of the present-day habits of certain species, among them one of the canaries (Linnaeous' *Serinus Canarius Serinus*), which has been attentively studied in recent years by E. Mayr, and which, in the course of a century, has carried out an expansional movement of this kind. For another thing, it is certain that the first occupant of a given area tries to keep it against all comers, and the size of the area varies according to its tenant's importance. A pair of eagles will need a whole mountain, while a family of robins or nightingales will be content with a barn or a suburban garden. For all that, their rule is nonetheless absolute, and their progeny have to rear their own families further off.

Also, we must remember that birds certainly appear to share a common origin with reptiles, whose prehistoric habitat was undoubtedly the warmer regions, as for the most part it still is.

Be that as it may, the first theory is the more generally accepted, and seems to be better confirmed by the habits of the majority of species. The birds of the tropics may be numerous, but we have only to think of some northern countries in the nesting season to recall those astonishing uncountable myriads of winged migrants that flock to them from every part. It certainly seems that there in the north is their natural home, and that there it has always been.

Yet it does not follow that the theory of a northern origin for migratory birds imposes itself by weight of incontrovertible evidence. It has met with serious objections.

Although a gradual cooling of the climate certainly seems to have taken place during the indicated periods, it is even more certain that no one bird could have noticed it in the course of its short life. This change did not supervene from one year to the next, but imperceptibly, in the course of several centuries, or even several millennia. At what moment would a bird decide that it was necessary to go into exile, by admitting that the temperature was dropping with an undeviating regularity and was not merely fluctuating?

Besides, how would it know that it would be better off elsewhere? Would not the warm winds coming from the south have induced it to head in that direction? Still, this suggestion is contradicted by facts based upon observation. Today an unaccustomed cold spell does not persuade the sedentary birds to seek a more favorable climate: they stay where they are, and if the temperature drops still further, they die on their own ground. This contemporary evidence is confirmed by that from the past, and paleontology shows us that species unable to adapt themselves to new conditions were destroyed in their normal surroundings, making no attempt to flee.

We have still to explain the laws that control the double journey, and to examine the influences that cause the bird to obey them.

## *Acquired Habit or Innate Desire?*

Here the convinced advocates of an innate and ir-resistible instinct have a great opportunity, and they would triumph easily if some insurmountable contradictions did not at once get in the way of their thesis. The most serious objection is this: if this instinct exists, as they maintain, all birds, or at least all birds of the same species, would be similarly affected, whereas what happens is just the opposite. Among larks from the same field, lapwings from the same marshes, and owls from the same woods, some are found to be sedentary, others seasonal visitors, and still others only in transit. The infallibility of the impulse proves itself nonexistent at every moment.

Errors of instinct, it will be said. Yet if instinct makes mistakes, it is, by definition, no longer instinct, and there is no longer any reason to invoke it. At least, there is no longer any reason to invoke it in such an absolute form. However, there are some facts that must be accepted on the evidence, and for which, in spite of much surmise, no explanation has ever been satisfactorily provided without recourse to instinct. Having said this much, baldly and unequivocally, we must certainly satisfy provisionally some of the other theories, and that is what we shall do here, where our task is only to summarize, with all possible impartiality, contemporary scientific opinion. Some scientists, all men of great worth, have spoken. We repeat what they have said, and leave the responsibility of choosing to the reader.

Many authors maintain that heredity plays an important role in the phenomenon of migration. C. Aubert shares this opinion, and summarizes it. According to him, it is the annual procession of the seasons "that each year leads to a change in the distribution of heat and humidity, and it is the annual repetition of these phenomena, and their periodic action, that has brought the element of precision into these inward and outward journeys by causing the same acts to repeat themselves, thus creating habits that are hereditary but seasonal."

On the other hand, this explanation is not accepted by a number of ornithologists, notably Americans, who, while also making migration depend on meteorological influences, maintain that each animal responds to these influences by an individual sensitivity.

For others, migrations "are determined by a number of emotional causes, such as fear, contentment, comfort, laziness and physical energy, and by causes in which reason and the will take part. . . . They are the outcome of manifold external and internal causes, and perhaps they are no more than one of the great manifestations of nature's energy" (Ménégaux).

Still others do not seek so far. Z. Gerbe tells us that migration is an innate need to travel simply for the sake of traveling. But is this really an explanation? And are we any the wiser once we have heard it?

Other theories rest on the influence and duration of the day, according to the seasons.

We say "to eat like a bird," but in fact we know that birds are heavy eaters, and that much of their activity is spent in hunting for food. Consequently they need long hours of daylight, since, except for the rare nocturnal species, they do not know how to find their food in the dark. Recent observations have shown that the shortness of our winter days is a frequent cause of mortality among caged birds, especially tropical species (for instance, the blue-bellied finches), since they do not have enough hours of daylight in which to satisfy their hunger.

It is a fact that many birds go to the other side of the equator to find the season that they have just left in our hemisphere, and that the majority experience nothing but perpetual summer.

It can even be said that certain of them are virtually ignorant of the night, such as those that migrate from one polar region to the other, only suffering a few moments of darkness during their double journey.

In the tropics, however, day and night are equal, and migrations take place just the same. So if this explanation has any value, once again it is not the whole story.

Bourdelle has expounded one of the most recent and important of these theories, which, while far from ending the debate, seems to have taken it a giant stride forward. And we owe it to Rowan, the American naturalist.

That observer, experimenting on some crows and buntings with the principal intention of demonstrating the influence of light, put the birds in a cage during the autumn, and, by controlling the lighting, temperature, humidity, supplies of food, and so on, surrounded them by a sort of artificial spring.

Rowan found that in the depths of winter their sexual excitation became what it would normally have become in April or May. He ringed his captives and released them. It can be imagined only too well what became of the buntings, but it was proved that the crows flew toward the north, reaching areas where they are never seen in winter.

Does this mean, then, that the swelling of the gonads is a cause of migration? By provoking this state mechanically a fever is induced, an obvious "migratory ecstasy." Here there is undeniably a connection between cause and effect, and it is surely relevant to what we have described earlier in other classes of animals.

Not to overwhelm the reader with quotations, we have only given some examples, and if in spite of everything the *why* of migration can still not be stated with certainty, perhaps we shall have better luck with the *how*.

### Have Animals Senses that We Lack?

Before answering the above question, let us see if animals' ordinary senses can satisfy all the requirements of their migrations.

As might be expected, the problem of distant orientation has stirred up the most heated arguments, and these go on continuously. It must be said in advance that, in spite of laudable efforts and the convictions of the advocates of each contending theory, the problem is far from resolved.

As regards the insects' faculty for finding their way, the great majority of modern entomologists agree in recognizing that sight and memory play the chief, if not the sole, part.

On this point their conclusions, based particularly on the study of ants and bees, appear to be correct; and despite a few factors that remain obscure, the same certainly seems true as regards birds, on evidence obtained by studying the behavior of carrier pigeons.

Of course, carrier pigeons must not be confused with migratory pigeons. In general, carrier pigeons are sedentary birds, which experience no periodic need to take journeys, and which have only to solve the relatively simple problem of returning to the nest, under conditions greatly modified by their preparation and training. They have nothing to do with the creatures we are studying, and strictly speaking, we should not cite them in this debate. So we will simply point out in passing that, although visual memory seems sufficient to explain their behavior almost completely, this has not prevented a great number of theories, sometimes most extraordinary ones, being proposed to interpret their "mysterious gifts."

To return to our migrants proper, do they also guide themselves solely by sight, which enables them to recognize a series of familiar landmarks on their long journey? Let us hear what some of the most outstanding observers have to say.

More than one of them would echo A. Mercier, speaking of storks: "It is certain that the old birds show the novices the way." And, indeed, so certain does this seem, that the opinion is commonly held.

The only thing wrong with it is that it is contradicted by the facts.

At Rossitten, Thienemann, also experimenting with storks, ringed some young ones taken from the nest and kept them captive beyond autumn, by which time all the adult birds had departed. Only then did he release his prisoners. They flew straight toward the south, and, checked at points en route as well as at journey's end, they were found to show the same proportion of successful flights as the parent birds would have shown. In this connection let us recall the experiments carried out at Heligoland, quoted earlier, where in 400 species studied, the young birds were always the first to arrive on the outward journey, i.e. on their first journey over a route necessarily unknown to them.

Yet, supposing that this instruction is really given, that all the parent birds do in fact show their young what direction to take, would it not be attributing to them a natural gift quite as marvelous as the pure instinct they are believed to have, if, as a result of a single outward journey, they could retain a memory of a route several thousand miles long faithfully enough to recognize all the landmarks the wrong way round, as it were, on their return? Visual memory on this scale would be a miracle, and if, reasonably, we want to discard all idea of the miraculous, the existence of such a memory seems a little hard to accept.

Besides, we have seen that migration is often undertaken by night. Then where are the landmarks? The visual-memory advocates reply that they are numerous. At the height at which the migrants fly, some lighted town is always within their horizon, or some lighthouse. Their opponents parry this by asking if—without going back to the start of the Quaternary, but, say, only half a million years—there have always been enough city lights and beacons to satisfy the migrants' needs.

And those that cross the vast ocean areas? Year by year

the Antarctic penguins swim great distances, and at that level their line of vision is restricted to a few yards, so that they cannot take a bearing on anything but the nearest wave. As for the bird that can soar to 16,000 feet, if at such an altitude it can see anything below, its horizon will lie at about 150 miles. Its destination, however, is much further off than that.

Too, some terns and Anous, released at sea at distances of 500 and 750 miles from their nest, returned to it. Pure chance, it has been said. However, the proportion of these returns—thirteen out of twenty-two in one case, and three out of five in the other—greatly exceeds the calculated probabilities, if accidents that could check or deflect the bird on so long a journey are taken into account.

However, none so deaf as those that will not hear. In controversies of this sort, it is sad to see how often the opponents of a theory will fasten upon any argument whatsoever rather than abandon a position once taken up. As regards our present subject, it has even been claimed that birds recognize their route by finding it clearly indicated by the wake of ships, and that they then have to do no more than follow it.

Even allowing this wake a visibility of two, or even four miles, which is certainly much exaggerated, the bird would still have to follow it across a space totally without reference points for another six or seven hundred miles, without deviating from it by so much as one second of arc! Thus the problem remains exactly the same, and surely we are not being difficult if we find this "explanation" unsatisfactory.

The part played by sight is so preponderant, some maintain, that the majority of migrants are held up by fog, or return to their starting point as if abandoning the journey. This is true, agrees the opposition, but not always true. Several species, among them larks and starlings, "fly through the fog" (C. Aubert). So the obstacle is not impenetrable, in which case the bird has another way of guiding itself.

Faced by these disagreements, what stand should be taken? Let us look into this further.

We have mentioned that migration depends on the wind. When it blows warm and humid from the southwest, the bird is given notice of a climate that suits it in that quarter, and it flies in that direction. A head wind does not stop it. On the contrary, many species migrate by flying against the wind.

However, many (or the same ones, on occasion) also migrate with the wind behind them, or with a cross-wind. Besides, if we put forward this attraction of a milder temperature to explain the southward migration of autumn, how is the opposite effect brought about on the return journey in the spring, in view of the dry, cold and disagreeable winds that blow from the north and the east? Must we postulate, according to the equinox, an autumnal thermo-hydrotropism and a vernal cryo-xerotropism? But, then what about such birds as the golden oriole and the swift, which leave us at the height of the hot weather, when such influences can have no effect?

Are we, then, to conclude that the five classic senses do not suffice to control migratory behavior? Have animals other senses, unknown to us?

From the time when experiments with terrestrial electricity and magnetism began to absorb scientific minds, there was no lack of attempts to find in them an explanation of birds' navigational gift. However, uncertainty persisted, and if an animal was to be compared to a compass, no one could discover where in its body it kept its magnetic needle.

It was about 1880 that Viguier revealed its existence and position, placing it in the semi-circular canals of the ear. The theory had considerable success, although experiments did not seem to confirm it in any way; and it goes without saying that it was also violently attacked. Neglected, and then revived, it came bounding back with more force than ever, thanks to the discovery of the Hertzian waves, and today it has some extremely learned advocates, among them J. Casamajor and G. Lakhovsky.

Certain "proofs" adduced by these authors do not seem entirely convincing, in spite of their disciples' enthusiasm. When Cassamajor stuffed his test pigeons with quinine sulphate, or poured warm wax into their ears, and cried: "Look at that! They no longer react to electromagnetic vibration!" we should certainly have been even more astonished if the unfortunate birds had reacted to anything at all. However, impartiality compels us to record some observations made in Spain and Germany in which it has been demonstrated that pigeons are completely disoriented in the vicinity of a powerful transmitting set at the moment of a strong discharge. In a similar instance the birds "swerved, wheeled round in circles that became increasingly wider, until finally they resumed their direct route once outside the wave's influence." As has been pointed out, although this example does not furnish a definite conclusion, it nevertheless seems to indicate that "the creature reacts to certain stimuli completely ignored by our senses, or at least by our consciousness."

Cathelin has summarized a theory he has long held, and which we in turn will try to expound.

For this scientist the problem is purely environmental, and not at all biological. It is a problem of control, and its solution must be sought by studying the atmosphere's electromagnetic galvanism.

Cathelin considers the bird a living barometer of extreme sensitivity, a "wonderful little jewel in the electromagnetic structure," which explains why it is so docilely obedient to the influence of the atmosphere's great equinoctial air currents, currents of great depth, which have their starting point at the equator. "This process can be compared to what happens to the warm air in the rooms of our homes, except that in this case the air's upward circular movement embraces the whole earth under the influence of the sun's heat." These currents are variable, due to nocturnal cooling and to evaporation, and at given moments they induce the bird to stop, since it is a prisoner of these phenomena and is "held in them as in a vise." The return journey is determined by: (1) the weakened equinoctial currents of the spring; (2) the memory; (3) the birds' panoramic view.

This thesis has been opposed by a number of objections, which Cathelin calls "trivial enough," but which we, if we are not to be accused of bias, must take into consideration.

For a start, can we say that the existence of these great atmospheric electrogalvanic currents, or at least their exact nature and the laws that control them, have been completely and definitely proved? Cathelin himself recognizes that terrestrial magnetism "is still very mysterious," and hopes that his studies "will explain thoroughly some facts hitherto obscure."

Again, if the influence of these currents is such that the bird cannot escape it, how is it that all birds are not equally subjected to it, and on exactly the same date? Cathelin replies that this is a question of adaptation. "It is the exception that creates the fresh factor. . . . Are we not ourselves migratory creatures, along with the Lapps or the Negroes? . . ." Then are we, it will be asked, guided by air currents?

And again, if this phenomenon has its starting point on the equator, how come the great majority of birds fly beyond the equator, and by a good deal, in one direction or the other? And how are we to explain those numerous east-to-west migrations, or the vertical ones? And all those that take place other than at the equinoxes? And, finally, supposing that the theory is true for the great autumnal migrations, are not the arguments that purport to explain the spring arrivals "trivial enough" in their turn?

Attempts have been made to prove these laws by experiment. Birds have been shut up at the time of migration in copper cages enclosed in turn in iron boxes with thick sides and equipped with perches to register the birds' movements. The experimenters thought they could detect a partial diminution of the birds' restlessness—and, once again, it would be astonishing if in such conditions there was not something of the sort, with or without magnetism! Without a doubt, this sort of experiment approaches those made in laboratories on an animal frightened by a situation it could never meet with in nature, and in which it is obliged, either from terror or constraint, to behave or not to behave exactly according to what it is hoped to prove.

Within the limits we have imposed on ourselves, we have tried to condense into these few pages a subject so vast that the numerous and important works devoted to it are still far from exhausting it. We do not pretend to have said everything, but equally we hope that we have omitted nothing essential.

Moreover, we have been careful to respect, in every possible measure, the opinions of each author quoted by us, no matter how contradictory. In questions of this sort it is a factious attitude, and certainly a foolish pretension, to claim with authority and conviction sole possession of the truth, when everyone knows that this is not so, and when an impartial examination of all published opinions will quickly show that much the same has been claimed for them (which is not to say that any one of them is completely wrong, but, surely, that none can be absolutely right!). Ever since man appeared, he has been stating hypotheses, and then he has been forced to contradict them by proposing others in their place, and so on, until he has had to return to his first ideas and start all over again. But this does not mean that all his labor has been lost. On the contrary. Each attempt marks a stage, and even the worst mistakes have served some purpose, if only by producing reactions so striking that they themselves have come to be generally accepted.

Impartiality does not keep us from having personal preferences, and here our intention has been to allow the reader the pleasure of choosing his own from all the conjectures offered. If we must state our own preferences, we would favor—at least as regards the higher vertebrates—an intelligence capable of judgment and selection within the somewhat restricted limits imposed by environment and the demands of the physical organism—an intelligence much less than that of man in quality, yet not so very different in quantity, and one that, although necessarily collective in the case of the most regimented creatures, retains some small part of individuality, enough to explain the contradictions, deviations, mistakes and also the advances exhibited by the behavior of the group as a whole.

Finally, if it is necessary for us to justify our caution, we can hardly do better than to continue to borrow the most useful reference from the best authority. In this case it is the opinion of one of the incontestable masters of modern ornithology, J. Berlioz: "So much has been written, and so many hypotheses and theories have been put forward regarding the origin of migration, that it seems extremely difficult to draw an exact and plausible conclusion, and all suppositions, whether involving an ancestral attraction of some kind, some unknown propulsive force or the phenomena of natural magnetism, believed to be able to give evident scientific explanations to the complex biology of migration, still remain completely devoid of practical foundation."

Under the aegis of such an eminent specialist, we feel ourselves much better authorized to ask to be excused our uncertainties.

# Index